The Egyptian Calendar

A work for eternity

The Egyptian Calendar
A work for eternity

Anne-Sophie von Bomhard

Periplus

London

© PERIPLUS PUBLISHING LONDON LTD, 1999
© English translation Periplus Publishing London Ltd 1999

First published in October 1999 by
Periplus Publishing London Ltd
4 Bedford Row
London WC1R 4DF

Editor: Danièle Juncqua Naveau
Production Manager: Allan Howard
Translation: Ludwig von Bomhard

ISBN 1-902699-05-X

Origination by The Colour Edge Group, London.
Printed and bound in Spain by SYL, Barcelona.

Acknowledgments

I wish to express first of all my gratitude to Professor Erik Hornung for his invaluable advice and his encouragement which have been of great help in the completion of this study of Egyptian calendarics, and for the generosity with which he opened his vast knowledge of the subject and which guided his kind remarks and reflections on my insufficiencies and all too peremptory statements.

My deepest gratitude goes to Professor Jean Yoyotte for the time he spent reading the text and the care which he took in digging out my errors and clumsiness; each of these encounters was a pure delight through the wonder, each time renewed, at his encyclopedic knowledge. If this book had only been a pretext for these work sessions, it would already be amply justified. But I am most particularly honoured by his offer to contribute an introductory comment which is my greatest reward.

I also wish to express my gratitude to those who made my work easier for me: Mrs Josette Dantier who seized and worked the text on the computer, for her precision and reliability; Mr. Francis Menès for his verifications of the scientific terminology; Mr. Kurt Locher for his generous offer to utilise both his work and his photographic archives. But above all I take great pleasure in expressing my deepest and heartfelt gratitude for his patience and unwavering support to my husband Ludwig von Bomhard, who took over the ungrateful task of taking up the text again and again in the course of my manifold modifications and innumerable corrections, and who in addition has accepted responsibility for the English and German versions.

This book would still never have seen the light of day without my publisher, Mrs. Danièle Naveau, a passionate amateur of Egypt and its mythology. To her competence as a publisher, Mrs Naveau adds a true and great artistic sense for the creation and layout of a book, as well as a talent for organisation and human relations which has secured Mr. Allan Howard, whose great talent as a true magician of computerised images is very much in demand. My gratitude to both for having brought out this book in a form, quality and beauty which I would not have believed possible.

Foreword

Where modern man wants to form an opinion of the Ancient Egyptians' knowledge of celestial mechanisms and the theories which they derived from them, he will have a difficult time because of the immense proliferation of legends and mythical parabolae, and will always find several different representations for one and the same subject or event. Thus, the sky is shown as the ceiling of a room resting on four pillars, but also as the starry body of a woman, the goddess Nut, whom her father Chu – the embodiment of Space – has separated from her husband Geb, the Earth. Then again, the sky is shown as the cow Hathor which has carried away Ra the Sun into the sky, henceforth swallowing him and then giving new birth to him every day, as does Nut… The two celestial bodies of day and night are considered as the eyes of the sky god: the moon is the left one, shown as the farded Eye of Horus, which is hurt by Seth and healed again by Thot. Thot, the ibis, however, is himself a lunar god, and so is Khonsou, etc... This "diversity in approach" was the Egyptians' roundabout way of describing the mysteries of the divine and the cosmos by poetic names and tales, which they use to talk about and to talk to the gods who determine the course of the cosmos and man's destiny. Yet, at the same time, this mystic poetry encapsulates a logical, coherent cosmography and its implicit physics.

The gods are usually shown in human form in the representations, sometimes with an animal head, differentiated by their headgear; they are frequently accompanied by their name in hieroglyphic writing. Thus the documents which Egyptian art has left us and which come closest to our maps of the sky, generally consist of a row of such personalities, shown in parallel horizontal registers, one beneath the other: planets and stars stand upright in boats which glide across the ocean of the sky, twelve such gods representing the months, and other stellar goddesses the hours. In addition, these figurative convoys contain some phantasmic compositions representing celestial configurations. Circular images of the nocturnal sky only appeared in the 2nd century B.C., when hellenistic astronomy introduced the signs of the zodiac into the original indigenous Egyptian iconography.

In the New Kingdom (between 1500 and 1100 B.C.), the classical astronomical representations were painted on temple ceilings, which were themselves images of the cosmos, and on the sepulchral vaults of kings[1], because the defunct monarch henceforth shared the perennial destiny of the sun. Also comparable to our astronomical tables, lists of names of the 36 decanal stars were painted inside the coffin at the beginning of the Middle Kingdom (around 2000 B.C.), to ensure the

---

[1] See Fig. 13 (Ramesseum ceiling) and Fig. 10 (Tomb of Senmut, favourite minister of Queen Hatshepsut).

celestial triumph of the deceased – so that the defunct could, as it were, read the sky from his position within. The hours of the night were defined by the movement of the decans across the sky[2] (showing in orderly mathematical fashion the decans as the abscissa, the hours as the ordinate).

The documents found on temples and tombs, on the basis of which the present study of the *Egyptian Calendar* is based, compound what may have been the cosmographic wisdom of the sacerdotal scribes, and are naturally drawing their deepest sense from the image of the world which led to the building of these mighty monuments of stone and the rich furnishings of the tombs of the high and mighty in the land.

In the *first time*, the sun Rah-Atoum created the Sky and the Earth out of the chaos of darkness and humidity which reigned before. He set up and shaped the fertile land of Egypt between the deserts, giving his favourite creatures a system which allowed them to morally and politically continue his creation. He conferred his power to a human monarch of his making and destined him for rule: Pharaoh. Meanwhile, Rah pursues his course far from the Earth, sailing along the heavenly river, ageing towards evening, rejuvenated during his nocturnal course through the nether regions and reappearing re-born and triumphant again at the rise of the new day. He is not without task though, such as to keep away the outer darkness, facing the dragon Apopi who tries to provoke his failure in this endeavour. Each mechanism of nature depends on this creator and on the gods issued from him. The energy and goodwill of the two higher beings, Rah and Pharaoh, must be maintained. Rah must live for the kingdom and its inhabitants to prosper, for all things to remain or return to their right place and order.

And the "*Son of Rah*" is destined to rule "*all that the sun touches on its course*" and to uphold the safety and prosperity of Egypt. On innumerable paintings on temple walls, it is always he who carries out the rituals which nourish and protect the gods, keeping them clear of the Evil and the Unclean. As compensation, the gods hand him the power and the strength to rule mankind, to conquer enemies, to uphold the law. It is up to his function as the head of both realm and army to raise or rebuild the sanctuaries and to assure the income necessary for the priests who, in practice, uphold the cult in his place and name. As the holy places which regulate the course of the universe, the temples' inner sanctae are built of solid stone. Chiselled inscriptions repeat to saturation the obligatory virtues of the king, or inscribe in stone for eternity conjurations and prayers, and what the gods answer them…

No matter whether or not Pharaoh is his predecessor's son, each ascension is a new morning for the world, a guarantee of order maintained. Such events as civil strife or enemy invasion are considered as the return to initial chaos; peace and victories as the return to the essential harmony issuing from Pharaoh "*who rises anew like Rah*".

---

[2] See Fig. 39.

History does not progress, it happens like an eternal commemoration of the creation.

Pharaoh nevertheless is mortal. Once he has died, he becomes a new Osiris, a great-grandson of Rah whom his brother assassinates and on whom his wife Isis, together with the Embalmer Anubis, has bestowed an indestructible capacity of survival and who now reigns in the nether regions. At the same time, however, he travels across the daily and nightly sky as an omnipresent god, together with his ancestor Rah the sun. These ways and means of bodily and supernatural survival thanks to embalming and the funereal magic are open to all in the realm – as long as the cosmos into which the dead are gloriously integrated, remains forever the same.

These gods Osiris, according to a ritual of the late period, are destined to "*walk through eternity* (neheh)", participating in all ceremonies and festivities in the course of the year.

Eternity: it is an oddity of the Egyptian language to possess two words to define it, and which are used both by themselves, or together. One can say *neheh*, "always" or *djet* "persistently", both words used together meaning something like "*for ever and ever*". The masculine word *neheh* in writing is defined by the sun and describes in a way its eternal cyclical movement. The female word *djet* is represented by the image of the Earth and describes an immovable consistency.

The year is called *renpet*, which derives from the verb *renep* "to be young, to rejuvenate" in the sense as does the world of plants and animals, of men and the gods and stars, and which is often interpreted as "new" in the context of the return of the flood of the Nile. The hieroglyphic sign describing this word, and serving as an ideogram for our "year", is a branch of the palm tree without leaves, on which a little excrescence represents a kind of notch. This is the simplified form which the gods present to the king to offer him hundreds of thousands of years, thousands of thirty-year jubilees: a promise of eternity. The hieroglyph describing the jubilee (*hebsed*) is often shown suspended from its upper tip. At the lower tip can be seen the tadpole (the symbol for 100,000), resting on a circular sign (*shen*) which represents the universe as Rah wanders across it and Pharaoh rules it. On this stem, Thot – the lunar god who reckons time, protector of the learned and the scribes, who possesses knowledge and administers the creation – and Sechat – the goddess who watches over the royal inscriptions and books, and architectural plans and drawings – count the years back into the past, and forward into the future.[3]

This pharaonic obsession with the Eternal, so evident in the architecture and the sacral and royal inscriptions, did not prevent the Egyptians from living from one day to the next as did all other human beings. And they worked out a calendar to find their way in the course of time, as did all other human communities.

---

[3] See front and rear cover.

The Greek travellers – Herodot in the 5th century, Diodorus Siculus and Strabo in the 1st century B.C. – had admired the Egyptians' mathematical clarity which never required to have recourse to such props as inserted days or additional months. One and the same calendar was used to date and record the deeds of kings, administrative events, private documents and liturgical feasts (even if some of these feasts were mobile within a month if tied to the full or the new moon). This calendar was called the "civil" one after a latin expression used by an astronomer of the 3rd century A.D., which was to represent it de facto as the official calendar of the state and its subjects.

The years in Egypt are not based on the notion of origin or foundation (like the Birth of Christ, the creation, or the first olympic games). Each new king's ascension opened a new era. Depending on the period, the year II of the reign began either 365 days after the ascension, or on the day following the last of the current year.

The year is separated into three seasons whose names represent the three major agricultural phases: the flooding of the land by the waters of the Nile (*akhet*), seed and growth of the new plants (*peret*) and harvest (*shemou*).

Each season spans four months of 30 days and each day is counted from 1 to 30. To these 360 days are added the 5 so-called 5 epagomene days, "*those beyond the year*", making up 365 days altogether. At the end of these 365 days, the "*Opening of the Year*" or New Year is celebrated.

As the actual course of the Earth around the sun lasts through another quarter of a day, however, the days, decades (10-day periods) and months wandered by one day every four years, by a decade every 40 years, by a month every 120 years, until after 1460 years, New Year's Day and the natural season fell again into their original place. Despite this displacement which could almost be called dis-etymological, this system of strict abstraction functioned during practically the entire length of the egyptian civilisation. The introduction of another, additional, epagomene day every four years, decided by the greek-macedonian Pharaoh Ptolemy III, remained stillborn in the indigenous temples and the use of the so-called civil year went on, even well after the roman conqueror had imposed his own Julian calendar in Egypt.

In principle, the civil calendar with months (derived from the lunar phases), set at equal lengths within the solar year (less $1/4$ day) was a simple calculating tool which could be followed automatically, and which required no confirming recourse to astronomical occurrences. And yet! And yet the Egyptians did use and celebrate another "Opening of the Year" in addition to the one which inaugurated the civil year. This other New Year's Day was determined by the observation of the heliacal rise of Sirius before the dawn of July 19. This star which we know under the latin name Sirius (*seirios in Greek*), is *Alpha* in the constellation of canus magnus of Orion the Hunter. It is one of the brightest stars in the night sky and its rise together with the sun falls into the month in which the life-giving waters of the Nile begin to rise. According to Ptolemy III's decree, "*the day of the appearance of Sothis is called the*

Opening of the Year in the Writings of the House of Life", i.e. according to the traditions of sacred knowledge. The Egyptian saw in this beneficial star the female goddess *Soptet* (*Sothis* in Greek), with the sign of a thorn (*seped*) above her, which served either to write her name or to decorate her with two high, standing feathers of a bird of prey. As the mistress of the flood she was associated with her near-homonym *Satjet* (*Satis* in Greek), the traditional Patroness of the region of the 1st cataract, but also with Isis herself, Osiris' wife, whose effluvium swells the river. Isis-Sothis, who was included in the constellation of Orion the Hunter in hellenistic days, was given the bitch as an attribute, the small bitch (*canicula*) whose appearance on the sky announces the hot period of the "dogs' days". The star Orion itself was represented as the god *Sahou* with the sign *sah*, a normal divine figure holding the usual sceptre[4].

Could the Egyptians have used different calendars? The so-called civil calendar built once and for all from the observation of the course of the sun and the phases of the moon, and in addition a "sothic" calendar based on the heliacal rise of Sirius? In very recent publications, an old, well thrashed out problem over astronomical problems, but also those of chronology, has been brought to life again. Shrewdly using these, Anne-Sophie von Bomhard submits here a new theory constructed on well-balanced analyses of the astronomical documents which depict Sothis, Orion and other stellar personifications, but also on the rare texts which actually mention the discrepancy between the two years. She very plausibly points out that the Egyptian observers and calculators can hardly have missed the fact that the year measures $365^1/4$ days and offers the hypothesis that with the pharaonic calendar they succeeded in including the cycles of the sun, of Sirius, and of the moon in one single system, in a Great Year of 1460 years – in a system which, far from eliminating the civil year, quite to the contrary, absolutely required that it be maintained.

The Egyptian Calendar: A Work for Eternity entirely conforms with the pharaonic system's manifold aspiration to perennity, regularity and stability of an eternally unchanging cosmos. A well thought-out construction which conforms to the continuity of a structure which rests in an untouchable tradition, but also in the familiar practice of everyday life. Mrs. von Bomhard's conclusions lead to the decisive question: what is the scope of this calendar she proposes – which in a way enhances again the long underestimated reputation of the Egyptian astronomers and mathematicians – concerning the further elaboration of the historiographic knowledge of the Egyptians about their own past? Reckoning with the years and months of the civil calendar was sufficient for the needs of political and administrative power centres and generations of normal citizens working for the very close and perhaps a little less close future, but who hardly needed to reckon in really long periods, neither forward, nor backward in time. Even the projects of the Pharaohs, except concerning their own posthumous perennity, could hardly lie in centuries, much less dozens of them. Except for new inventory revelations, it would hardly appear likely that the Egyptians – contrary to the pre-columbian central american Indians – could determine

---

[4] See Fig. 14 to Fig. 20.

the periods in which would arrive times of interregnum of internal strife, decline and poverty. On the other hand, the scribes very busily tried to document the high age of their country, as *the royal canon of Turin* demonstrates, which reaches back to the divine dynasties and enumerates ancient kings and their years and months of reign. No matter how precise were their sources and the interpretations they drew from them, this far-reaching endeavour required a calendar of centuries, of which one may well wonder whether it was sothic or civil.

Jean Yoyotte

A remark: the statement contained in a note on Aratus, namely that the Egyptian kings on their accession swore a formal oath in the temple of Isis not to change the calendar (see p. 9), could really only relate to the Ptolemys of the 2nd or 1st century B.C., if it is not an invention of some Greek or Roman writer. Before that time, there hardly existed important Isis Temples and the new kings had their investiture confirmed by such essential deities as Amon in Thebes, Rah in Heliopolis, Ptah in Memphis. The only period in which a famous Temple of Isis could appear as a dynastic sanctuary is the hellenistic one; it could be envisaged that the Lagide Pharaohs, after the short-lived reform of Ptolemy III, expressed their respect and adherence to the priestly traditions in the great Iseion of Alexandria.

Table of Contents

Preface

A great number of publications in recent years bear witness to the renewed interest in texts of the pharaonic period which relate to matters of astronomy and the calendar. New ideas could only blossom, however, because the groundwork had been laid, the field had been ploughed and the earth sown well before. To begin with, there had been those who had contributed to the collection of data: in addition to the admirable compilations prior to Champollion – and those he contributed himself – must be mentioned above all the Thesaurus by Brugsch and the lovely publication by O. Neugebauer & R.A. Parker. As regards synthetic work on the calendar and Egyptian chronology, the road was opened by E. de Rougé, J.B. Biot, J.A. Letronne, R. Lepsius, E. Meyer, L. Borchardt, R. Weill, S. Schott and R.A. Parker.

Current research points in several directions. Some authors chose a technical approach like Ch. Leitz; then there are those, like A. Spalinger, who concede great latitude to mythology; others again associate with both approaches, like J. von Beckerath or R. Krauss, and they do indeed appear complementary rather than contradictory. For the development of this exposé, we have therefore chosen to follow the structure usually observed in the great Egyptian astronomical representations.

This study is limited to the outlines of the calendar and is conceived with a two-fold purpose. The first one is to submit a new theory on the general organisation of the calendar, based on the Greek and Egyptian texts as well as Egyptian astronomical representations. The second and more ambitious one is to evoke enough curiosity to attract new disciples to this branch of Egyptology, which seems thus far restricted to a few specialists. In order to achieve this, we have preferred a schematic approach giving priority to images wherever possible. We have kept Egyptian chronology altogether out of the framework of this research. Nevertheless, such aspects of the calendar as may be considered pertinent for chronological determinations have been outlined.

We also wish to point out in this introduction that for the ancient Egyptians, knowledge and science were inseparably linked with their religion, but that the mythological images which express them must never obscure in our eyes the solid and profound knowledge which lies hidden beneath them. It is the great and foremost task of any scientist to observe life and Nature, in order to understand their underlying laws: the founder of chromosomic research – which will revolutionise medicine in the coming decades – was a monk who observed the various plants of smooth and wrinkled peas in his kitchen garden and derived from them the principles of modern genetics.

The old Egyptians were past masters of observing nature and clearly possessed knowledge of a very high order in such disciplines as medicine, architecture, physiology, animal biology, mathematics and astronomy.

For the scientist, it is one of the most fascinating tasks to extract this knowledge from their mythological texts and images. It is thus that through the research of the documents which over millennia were painted on the walls of temples and tombs, if not hewn into rock, following the paths of adoration, faith and fears of this learned people of priesthood, along those of the mythical gods like Rah, Osiris and Isis, that this new theory of the astronomical calendar gradually grew.

Fundamental Notions

I. In search of eternity

For the Egyptians, the sky is symbolised by the feminine deity Nout. She can be found in many representations, her body entirely composed of stars, arched over the Earth, resting on her four members which symbolise the four pillars of the sky (Fig. 1). Her position reflects the outline of the hieroglyph for the sky: ▭

Earth is shown as a masculine deity, stretched on the ground beneath her. Standing between Sky and Earth is The Radiating Energy Shu, one of the aspects of the sun, who upholds Nout with both arms raised.

According to this cosmogonic vision[1], the sky and not the Earth is the Mother, the Nurse, wet nurse to Pharaoh and of Egypt. The sky is thus sometimes represented as a suckling cow whose spotted coat recalls the starry sky (Fig. 2).

The two celestial sources of light, the sun and the moon, are sometimes also designated as the "Eyes of Horus", the right eye being the sun, the left one the moon[2].

"As long as lasts the sky" is a term frequently found[3] in Egyptian texts; it should be understood as "as long as last the cycles of the sun and the moon", "for ever and ever".[4]

The quest for eternity is the most essential preoccupation of the Egyptian civilisation: monuments are built for millennia, texts constantly evoke perpetuity; the hieroglyphs themselves – their Egyptian name signifies "divine words" – engraved

---

[1] Which, incidentally, is a realistic view because the energy necessary for all forms of life does indeed come out of the sky, in the sun's rays.

[2] The left eye, wounded by Seth, progressively rebuilds again to become the healthy eye, i.e. the full moon (see infra, chapter The Moon)

[3] The cover reproduces the words of Thoth (Hermes), assuring Ramses II of the perennity of the monuments he has built. "As long as lasts the sky", the image perfectly illustrates the meaning: Thoth is counting the years on the hieroglyph signifying "year" ⸁, where the multiple notches stand for a great number; on top, the year sign reaches the hieroglyph for the sky, ▭ which crowns the text.

[4] Two different words are often associated to designate eternity: *nḥḥ* and *ḏt*; the *nḥḥ* eternity is often linked to the sun or the sky, the *ḏt* eternity to the moon or the Earth.

Fig. 1 - The Sky and the Earth (from a reproduction of the burial papyrus of Djed-Khonsou-iouf-ankh, original in Egypt. Museum Cairo)

Fig. 2 - The Celestial Cow
(18th dynasty, Egypt. Museum Cairo)

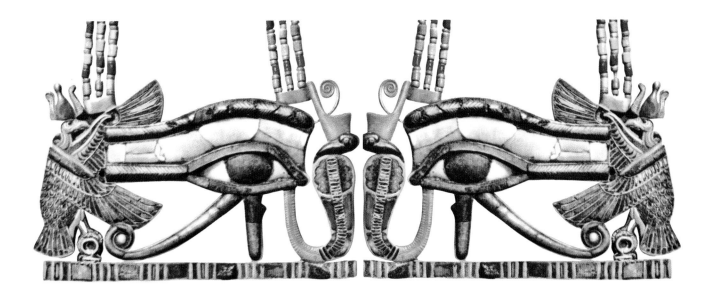

Fig. 3 - The two eyes of Horus (sun and moon)
from Tut-ench-amon's breastplate, 18th dynasty

into stone, are intended to resist the passage of time. This vision of the longest possible duration is the foundation of all human endeavour, because the Egyptian "sees far".[5]

But for him, the future is inseparable from the past and his concept of the universe is anchored in the certainty that to preserve life, it is imperative to uphold the initial order of the world by continuously fighting disorder and chaos.

For the comprehension of the calendar, it is

Fig. 4 – "...hundreds of thousands of annual cycles". Luxor, 19th dynasty (Photo by the author)

important to emphasise that for the Egyptians, its validity over very long periods of time is very clearly the foremost feature required. But in addition, it must be stressed that, in the Egyptian mind, Time and Eternity are not linear concepts, but cyclical ones: the monument on the book cover shows in its lower part (Fig 4) the sign of the year ⸙, posed on a tadpole (with the value of 100,000), itself perched on the sign symbolising the cycle ☋; this same symbol, called cartouche, encloses the names of the Pharaohs, lending them eternity.

In Egypt, the annual cycle is closely tied to the life of its river. What makes the outstanding originality of this country, where it practically never rains, is that all agriculture depends on the flooding of the Nile, which irrigates the soil and fertilises the earth with the silt it carries with it. In July, the rising waters arrive from the deep South, reach the Nile Delta, and gradually descend again towards October, leaving the soil rich and soft, ready for plentiful harvesting. These four months of inundation constitute the first of the three seasons in the Egyptian calendar, which are created around the flood:

> 1st season: The Nile flooding
> 2nd season: Seeding and growth,
>   translated into Greek as Winter
> 3rd season: Harvest, translated into Greek as
>   Summer

The extent of the flood caused abundance or short thrift. Nilometers were installed all along the river, to enable its measurement, and stone-engraved annals dating as far back as the Old Kingdom state the heights in ells to which the water rose each year.

The Egyptians had noticed very quickly that the arrival of the flood coincided with the annual renewed appearance of the brightest star in the sky: Sirius, whose Egyptian name "Sopdet" was transmitted to us in its Greek form of "Sothis".

The recognition of the annual cycle and its definition, the linking of celestial phenomena to terrestrial happenings, are essential preliminaries to establishing any kind of calendar. This enterprise requires long prior observation of the sky and the stars, as well as the recording, in writing, of these observations, in order to verify them over long periods of time. It is quite natural, therefore, that the divine tutors of Time and Calendar should be Thoth[6], God of Science and Seshat, Goddess of Writings and Annals (Fig. 5).

---

[5] The word *sr*, meaning high government officials, also designates the long-necked giraffe, "the one who sees far".

[6] On the various names of Thoth relating to time, see M. Clagett, Ancient Egyptian Sciences I, p 304.

Fig. 5 - Thoth and Seshat, Science and Writing,
Luxor, 19th dynasty (Photo by the author)

II. Calendars: their uses and difficulties

1. The usefulness of calendars

A calendar has two main functions:

1.1 The measure of time

Before all else, calendars serve to measure the passage of time: to add up the passing years or to count the number of years separating two events.

1.2 The detection of cyclic phenomena

Calendars must allow the recognition of regularly recurring events and the definition of their periodicity – such as the seasons or the phases of the moon. It is their organisation in relation to one or another such cycle which distinguishes various different calendars (lunar, solar, or stellar calendars).

The cycle of the sun

The solar year, also called natural or tropical year, is defined by the lapse of time which separates the two same equinoxes or solstices. Its duration is currently[1] of 365.242192643, rounded off to 365.2422 mean solar days.

Equinoxes and solstices determine the seasons on which all agricultural life depends; naturally therefore, men had very early-on created calendars derived from the cycle of the sun.

The cycle of the moon

is determined by the different phases of the moon during its full revolution around the Earth, which has an average duration of $29^1/_2$ days and determines the lunar month. The addition of 12 lunar months thus forms a lunar year of 354 days.

Calendars organised on the basis of a lunar cycle (e.g. the Islamic calendar) have the advantage of a short periodicity, but they diverge quickly from the seasons (in 36 years, any given month moves through the entire year). This discrepancy of more than 11 days in relation to the solar year requires the addition of a 13th month every three years. And finally, lunar calendars are particularly imprecise when it comes to computing the years over longer periods.

The cycle of the stars

The sideral year is the time between two appearances of the same star during two consecutive passages of the Earth through the same point of her orbit. On average, it has a duration of 365.2560 mean days[2]. It is thus longer than the natural or tropical year, the difference being due to the phenomenon called "the precession of the equinoxes"[3].

The cycles of the planets

The other planets in our solar system follow their own movements which set them apart from the stars, with different cycles and cyclical periods for each of them. They are of little interest for the elaboration of a calendar, but they can afterwards be integrated into an existing calendar construction.

---

[1] The tropical year decreases by about $^1/_2$ second per century.

[2] For Sirius, see infra, the sothic year.

[3] The Earth is not perfectly spherical, it flattens at the poles and bulges a little along the equator, due to its proper rotation. The gravitational forces operating on this equatorial bulge by the sun and other celestial objects is gradually altering the inclination of the Earth's axis of rotation. This causes the axis to run through a cone in the opposite direction to the orbital movement of the Earth, requiring 25760 years for a complete cycle. Due to this phenomenon, the points where the celestial equator meets the equinoxial points are moving and causing the tropical year to be shorter than the sideral year by approximately 20 minutes.

2. Difficulties of calendars

Several problems can hinder the establishment of a calendar, mainly:

2.1 The incompatibility of astronomical cycles

The different cycles: solar, stellar, lunar, or planetary all present different lengths of period; a calendar perfectly suited for one of them would thus automatically be out of phase with any other. Developing a unique calendar which would take into account all the principal cycles is therefore an endeavour fraught with vast and very complex difficulties.

2.2 The fractions of days

The most problematic point lies in the fact that the cycles do not add up to a full number of mean days. The Earth's rotation, on the other hand, produces in the most obvious and inevitable way a succession of full days and entire nights which appear totally disengaged from any other phenomenon relating to the Earth's movements on her orbit, or from those of her lunar satellite. If we ignore the fractions of days in each cycle, they will accumulate over the years, add up to entire days, and provoke discrepancies big enough to impose re-adjustments in order to tally again with the original astral phenomenon on which the entire structure is based. The entire sense, purpose and principal quality of any calendar, however, must be its validity over long periods of time.

III. The Egyptian calendar: singularities, incoherences and paradoxes.

"...Let us derive strength from the assurance that where facts are concerned, no contradiction can remain irreducible in the end." [1]

R. Weill

The year normally used by the Egyptians in their administrative documents is the so-called civil year[2], composed of 3 seasons of 4 months each, i.e. 12 months of 30 days, to which are added five extra days called *epagomenoi* by the Greeks. This year of 365 days is called "mobile" or "vague" due to the fact of its travelling in the true year[3]: too short by almost one quarter of a day, it consequently quickly provokes a discrepancy in the seasons, which reaches almost one month in 120 years, that is to say in three or four generations[4].

Despite this very obvious discrepancy, however, the mobile year continued in use over several millennia, throughout the entire length of Egyptian history. This is even more surprising in view of the fact that a fixed, sothic year was perfectly well known. Beginning with the heliacal rising[5] of Sirius, this year is called "fixed" as opposed to the "mobile" year, because its length[6], which is very close to that of the tropical (natural, solar) year, avoids any discrepancies with the seasons' progress. Its habitual use could thus have kept the seasons in their rightful place. Preceded by some ten days by the rise of the Orion constellation at the end of the year (Fig. 6), the annually recurrent rise of Sirius at the beginning of the fixed year was observed with particular acuity[7], because it heralded the flooding of the Nile. And yet, any mention of the star's rise over the morning sky is found only sporadically in the known documents[8]. Clearly, the sothic year has never replaced the civil year in the administrative usage of the Egyptian clerks.

Nevertheless, one can easily confirm that the Egyptians were clearly conscious of the irksome character of the mobile year and deplored its inconveniences[9]. The vague year is qualified as "bad" and "incorrect": 𓏲𓏤𓃀𓎡𓏏𓅪 in Papyrus Anastasi IV, a term which Weill[10] showed as opposed to the "perfect", "correct" year: 𓏲𓏤𓄤𓆑𓂋𓏏 of Papyrus Chester Beatty I[11]. The use of these two adjectives, as well as

---

[1] R. Weill, *Chronologie*, p. 143.

[2] For the structure of this civil year, see Appendix I. p.90

[3] The length of the tropical year can be rounded up to 365.2422 days.

[4] It should be recalled at this point that the Gregorian Reform of the Julian Calendar became unavoidable at a time when that discrepancy had reached just 11 days.

[5] See the chapter on the heliacal rise. R.A. Parker, *Calendars*, in his theory, qualifies the fixed year inaugurated by the rise of Sirius as "lunar". He is followed in this by numerous authors, including most recently L. Dupuydt, *Civil Calendar and Lunar Calendar in Ancient Egypt*. We prefer to maintain the word "sothic" for this fixed year, and to reserve the term of "lunar" for what can beyond any doubt be attributed to the lunar cycle.

[6] The sothic year has a duration of 365¼, i.e. 365.2500 days.

[7] Sirius is already mentioned in the texts of the Pyramides, especially Spells 965, 1123, 1707; see also R. Krauss, *Astronomische Konzepte*, p. 146 ff.

[8] See chapter on the sothic period, p.40

[9] R. Weill, (*Chronologie*, pp. 30, 107-111) mentions among other texts the passage in Anastasi IV, 10,1 to 10,5 (*LEM* p. 45): *"Come to me, oh Amon! Save me of this upset year (gbt). It happened that the sun did not rise, that winter arrived in summer; month follows month in the wrong order, the hours are disrupted"*. When this papyrus was written (19th dynasty), however, the discrepancy was very small, which indicates that events are mentioned which happened almost 700 years earlier.
The Decree of Canopus (line 21 and following of the hieroglyphic text): *"...so that it may not happen that the feast days solemnly celebrated in winter should arrive in summer... and that others among those now celebrated in summer may not fall into winter in times to come..."*

[10] *RdE* V, 1946, pp. 255-256.

[11] P. Chester, Beatty I (reverse C I, 1-2): *"...see there, alike to the divine star which rises at the beginning of the perfect year (nfr)"*. Clearly, the term is used for the Sirius year. Regarding the association of *nfr* with *rnpt* see H. Brugsch, *Thesaurus* pp. 103 and 107; P. Germond, *Les invocations à la bonne année au temple d'Edfou*, Aegyptiaca Helvetica 11, especially pp. 79-80. The "good year" is, in fact, the sothic year. The term *nfr* has the sense of "complete", "accomplished", whereas the term *gbt* means "fractioned", "diminished".

Fig. 6 - Orion ⋯ in the most ancient known text of the Pyramids.

Unas Pyramid, 5th dynasty (Photo Kurt Locher)
King Unas is assimilated to Orion-Osiris (end of the year).
Central column: "In your (Unas') name of He-who-is-Orion,
As thy time shall follow Sky, thy time shall follow the Earth"

the tone of the texts cited above, demonstrate that the Egyptians were clearly aware that the sothic year remained linked to the natural year, whereas the mobile year moved away from it. It is indeed strange that this criticised vague year was not quickly replaced by the fixed, sothic year which was qualified as perfect. Even more surprising must appear that, to believe a passage of the latin scholar of Germanicus' translation of Aratus[12], to maintain the mobile year of 365 days seems to have been considered even as an obligation:

"...*when they acceded to the throne, the kings of Egypt, on the occasion of their coronation, had to swear a formal oath in the Temple of Isis that they would neither introduce a month nor even a day, nor ever alter the date of a feast day, but would continue to measure the 365 days as decreed by the Ancients.*"

This inadequacy of the usual, vague year to follow the course of the sun must appear even stranger in view of the all-pervading presence of the sun in Egyptian theology. As the dominant subject of cults and rituals, it is represented in every conceivable divine form on the walls of temples, its course across the sky is detailed for each hour on the walls of tombs and the sides of coffins. In addition, the sun is ever-present in ceremonies, writings and royal protocol. The king is identified with it, the same terms are used for both: Pharaoh and the sun alike rise (h^c) and vanish (htp) on their horizon (Fig. 8), the king is eternal like the sun (mi-R^c-dt). Strange indeed that this cult of the sun should find no reflection in the calendar.

There is, finally, another disconcerting point: the criticism formulated by the Egyptians themselves on the subject of their mobile calendar stands in stark contrast to the laudatory comments made by most Greek authors, e.g. Herodot[13], who writes about the Egyptians:

[12] Aratea 285 "...et jurejurando adigitur neque mensem neque diem intercalandum quem in festum diem immutarent, sed CCCLXV dies peracturos, sicut institutum est ab antiquis. (cited e.g. in Brunet de Presle, *Examen critique des dynasties égyptiennes*, p. 31; J.A. Letronne, *Nouvelles Recherches*, pp. 10-11; E. Meyer, *Chronol. Egypt.*, transl. Moret, p. 39; R. Weill, *Chronologie*, p. 57-58).
[13] Herodot II, 4.

"...their calendar is in my opinion better than that of the Greeks, because these introduce an intercalary month every two years, in consideration of the seasons, whereas the Egyptians, with their twelve months of thirty days, add five supernumerary days to each year, so that the cycle of the seasons always appears at the same date for them".

Herodot's conclusion is paradoxical, to say the least, when we think of the disruption of the flow of seasons engendered by the mobile year of 365 days.

The persistent problem for Egyptologists is

---

[14] *Chronologie* pp. 133-135. As R. Krauss, *Sothis und Monddaten*, p. 201, puts it: "one can no longer maintain that the Egyptians did not realise the lack of ¼ day in their mobile year". See also M. Clagett, *Ancient Egyptian Science* II, p. 37, on the knowledge of the length of the solar year, probably dating back to pre-dynastic times.

clearly stated by R. Weill[14]: **Why did the Egyptians, who since the most ancient times knew the fixed year, inaugurated by the rise of Sirius over the morning horizon, nevertheless continue to use the mobile year, whose inconveniences they recognised and indicated?**

This theory on the calendar proposes to explain this apparent contradiction and to demonstrate that the system did, in fact, imperatively imply the continued use of the mobile year. According to this theory, the mechanism of the Egyptian calendar is based on two essential facts: that the heliacal rise of Sirius inaugurates the fixed year, and the way to account for the extra quarter day of the sothic year.

Everything is, in fact, centred around Sirius, which is precisely the focal figure of a great many astronomical tables and representations.

Fig. 7 - The Horus of Edfu (Photo by the author)

Fig. 8 - The Great Pyramid called: "Horizon of Cheops" (Photo by the author).

Fig. 9 - Akhenaton and Nofretete rendering grace for the sun's gifts. 18th dynasty, Egypt. Museum Cairo
(Photo Lehnert & Landrock, succ. K. & E. Lambelet).

IV. Calendar texts and representations

Some texts which are of great importance for the study of Egyptian astronomy, or for considerations of chronology, may be of lesser value for the exact understanding of the structure of the calendar. As an example, the tables of the decans decorating certain coffins from the 9th or 10th dynasty[1], as well as from the Middle Kingdom, and the rising stars on the Ramesside[2] tombs, provide interesting astronomical information, but contribute little to the structure of the calendar itself. The documents known as the Calendar of Lucky and Unlucky Days, the Papyrus Cairo 86637[3] or Sallier IV[4] are no more explicit: for each day of the year, after indicating its beneficial or nefarious character, they enumerate the mythological event attached to it, with advice about what to do and what to avoid.

More explicit, however, are the tables containing decans as well as planets, Sirius, and the lunar deities, all of which could well point in the direction of calendar representations, or at least suggest that the way in which the celestial objects are shown could bring light to some calendar relations.

These tables are found on various kinds of monuments: in the royal tombs and burial temples, they evoke the destiny of the King which is not only solar, but stellar and cosmic as well. Temples dedicated to the gods, like those to burials, are a reflection of the world. Their floor is the Earth, their columns represent the vegetation which reaches up towards the sky, represented by the ceiling – and it is generally on the ceilings that we find these great astronomical representations. Nevertheless, a marvellous object in the Cairo Museum, a clepsydra or water clock called the "Karnak clepsydra", is also decorated with such astronomical pictures.

Sorting these monuments, we can enumerate:

- **The ceiling of the tomb of Senmut**[5] (Fig. 10). The southern part of this ceiling (the upper part of the painting), presents the names of the stars and the planets. The northern (lower) part gives the names of the months and the lunar deities.
- **The water clock of Karnak** dating from Amenhotep III[6] (Amenophis in Greek, Fig. 11, 46), shows three registers: the upper one with the stars and planets, the middle one with the lunar deities, and the lower one where the king is shown before the divinities of the month.
- **A variety of representations** on the panels and walls of the temples (Edfu, Dendera, Esna, Kom Ombo)[7], and more particularly the ceiling of the Ramesseum[8] (Fig. 13) show the same three registers as the Karnak clepsydra.
- **Paintings in some tombs**, one of the most beautiful and best preserved being that of Seti I[9].

Although varying in the details (names of decans, planets present or not), these great tables ranging from the 18th dynasty down to the latest times, are set up in remarkably similar fashion, the most complete ones being the water clock of Karnak and the ceiling of the Ramesseum, which disposed of three superimposed horizontal registers:

1 See O. Neugebauer & R.A. Parker, *EAT* I, pp. 1-21 and Plates 1-23; K. Locher, *JHA* n° 23, pp. 201-207 and *Middle Kingdom Astronomical Coffin Lids, Extension of the Corpus from 12 to 17 Specimens Since Neugebauer & Parker*, in C. Eyre, Transactions of the 7th International Congress of Egyptologists, OLA, pp. 697-702.
2 Especially the tombs of Ramses VI, Ramses VII and Ramses IX: see O. Neugebauer & R.A. Parker, *EAT* II, Plates 1 to 28.
3 Published by A.M. Bakir, *The Cairo Calendar*, as well as more recently by Ch. Leitz, *Tagewählerei*.
4 Select Papyri III, Plates 144-168; F. Chabas, *Le calendrier des jours fastes et néfastes de l'année égyptienne*; Ch. Leitz, *Tagewählerei*. For other references on these calendars see A. Spalinger, *Three studies*, p. 55, Note 20.
5 O. Neugebauer & R.A. Parker, *EAT* I, Plate 25; III Plate 1.
6 *EAT* III, plate 2 and *Ramses the Great*, Exhibition catalogue, 1976, pp. 140-147.
7 *EAT* III, Plates 29 to 44.
8 *RdE* 10, Plate I between pp. 16 & 17 and *EAT* III, Plate 5.
9 *EAT* III, Plate 3, and E. Hornung, *The Tomb of Pharaoh Seti I*, pp. 236-241.

1 - the first, upper register includes Sirius, the decans and the planets,

2 - the middle one shows the constellation of the northern sky and the lunar divinities,

3 - the third, lower register represents Pharaoh honouring the divinities of the months. On the ceiling of the Ramesseum the King, wearing a disk on his head, is himself assimilated to an astral deity.

Most of the other tables are composed of only the two first, properly astronomical, registers with the southern star Sirius in the upper one and the constellations of the northern sky below, according to the habitual Egyptian orientation:

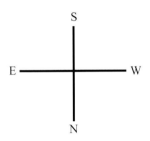

East and West are, on some monuments, inverted[10] but Sirius, the planets and the decans are invariably seen to move from East to West as they appear to do in the sky. The orientation of the hieroglyphs composing the names of the decans permits the verification of the direction of their movement.

We shall adopt the order of the Egyptian representations as the basic plan of progress for the study of the calendar.

A - The Upper Register
- Sirius and the sothic year,
- The cycle of the decans,
- The planets

B - The Lower Register
- The cycle of the moon.

---

[10] One must also distinguish between the orientation of the monument itself and that of the figurative elements.

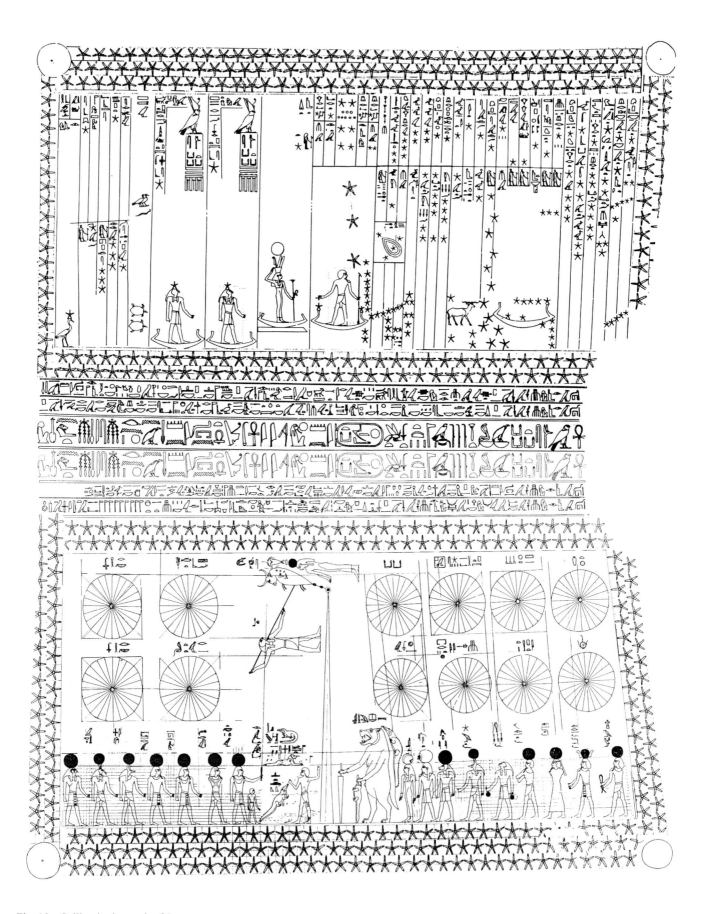

Fig. 10 - Ceiling in the tomb of Senmut

Fig. 11 - The Karnak water clock, Egypt. Museum Cairo Nr. 37525.

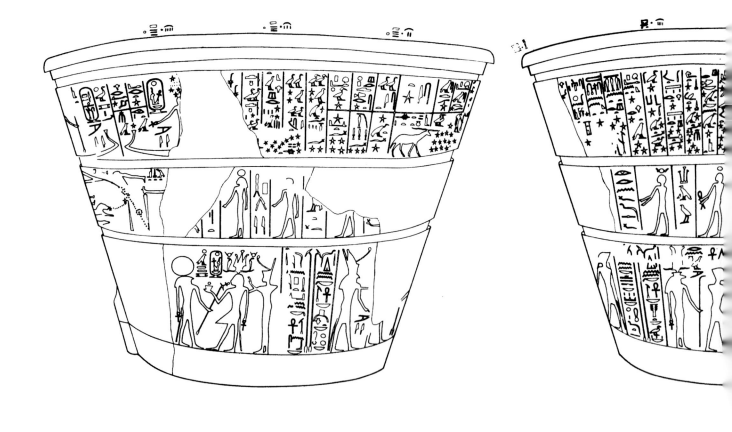

Fig. 12 - The Karnak water clock (from *Ramsès le Grand*, Exhibition catalogue), Paris, 1976.

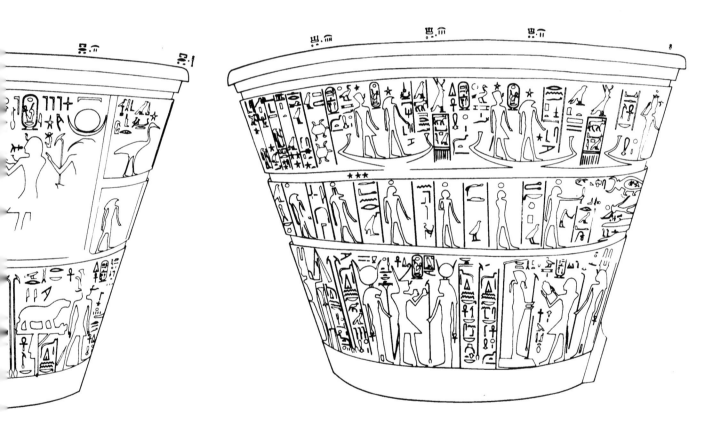

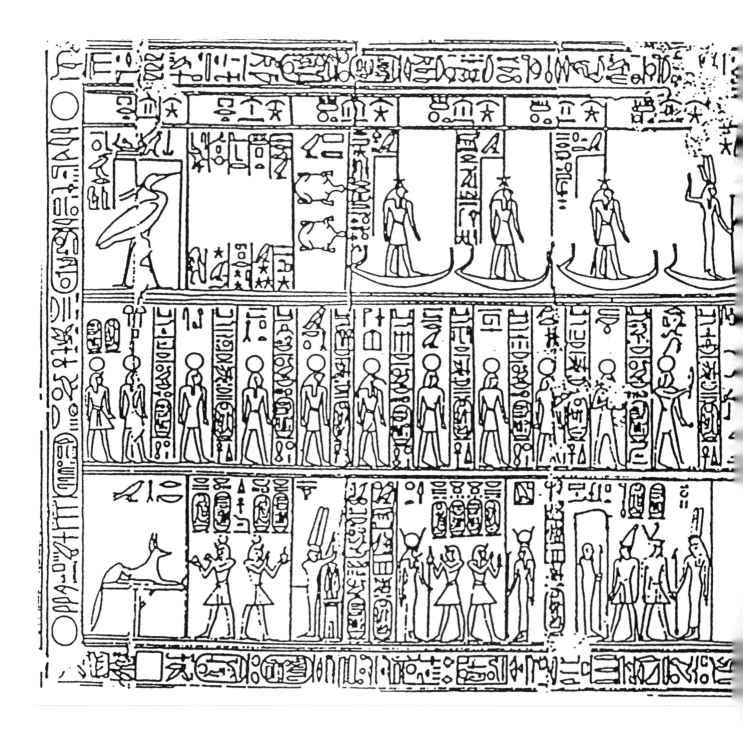

Fig. 13 - Ceiling of the temple of Ramses II in Luxor

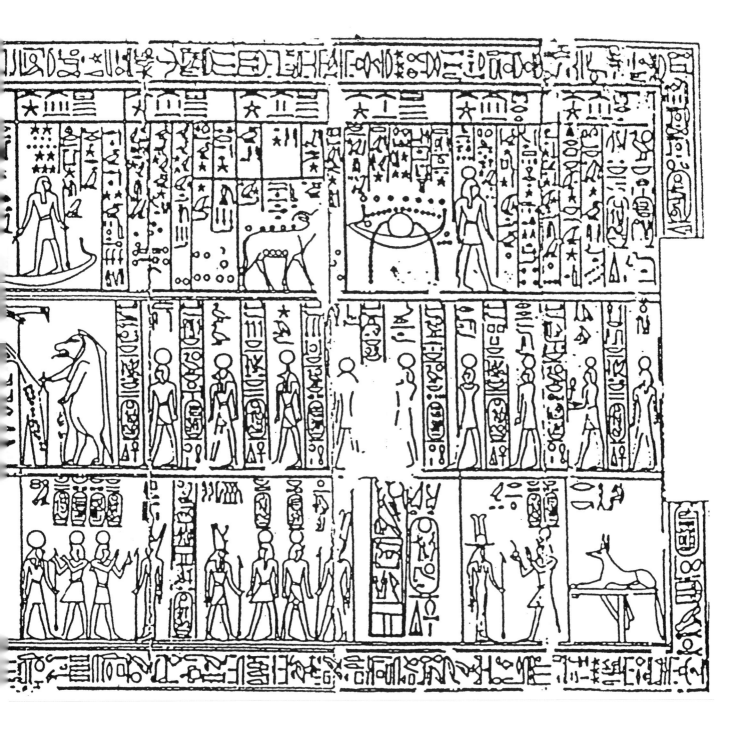

Calendar representations

A - Upper register

I. Sirius

1. Sirius in the representations,

2. Sirius and the sothic year,

3. The calendaric set-up: structure and conception

    of the gliding calendar,

4. The sothic period,

5. Latitude of reference for the heliacal rise of Sothis

II. The Decans

III. The Planets

B - Lower register

IV. The Moon

I. Sirius

1. Sirius in the representations

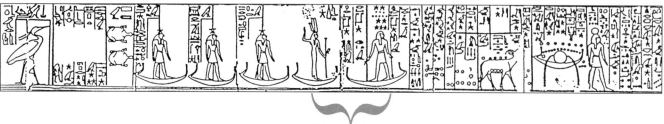

Fig. 14 - Ceiling of Ramesseum upper register

Sirius and Orion

Sirius and Orion invariably hold the centre of the upper register, seemingly dominating the whole. The images of the Ramesseum (Fig. 14) and the Tomb of Senmuth (Fig.15) are very similar in the attitudes, costumes and attributes. Sirius is shown standing in a boat, in the form of the goddess Isis, as indicated by the name written before her: Isis 𓊨 , Sopdet 𓊹. She faces Orion 𓂃, standing in his boat, with three stars close together above him, and the names of the stars which compose the constellation.

Their images differ in some details from older reproductions found on the coffins of the 9th, 10th, 11th and 12th Dynasties[1] (Fig. 16). There, each one carries the hieroglyph of his name as a crown, and the two sceptres face each other, whereas in the New Kingdom that of Orion has changed place (Fig. 15).

O. Neugebauer and R.A. Parker[2] suggest that the change in the disposition of the sceptres could reflect a new order of the decans of the Orion group, and K. Locher[3] believes that the joined sceptres represent decan Nr. 28 *ꜥbwt*. The latter also places

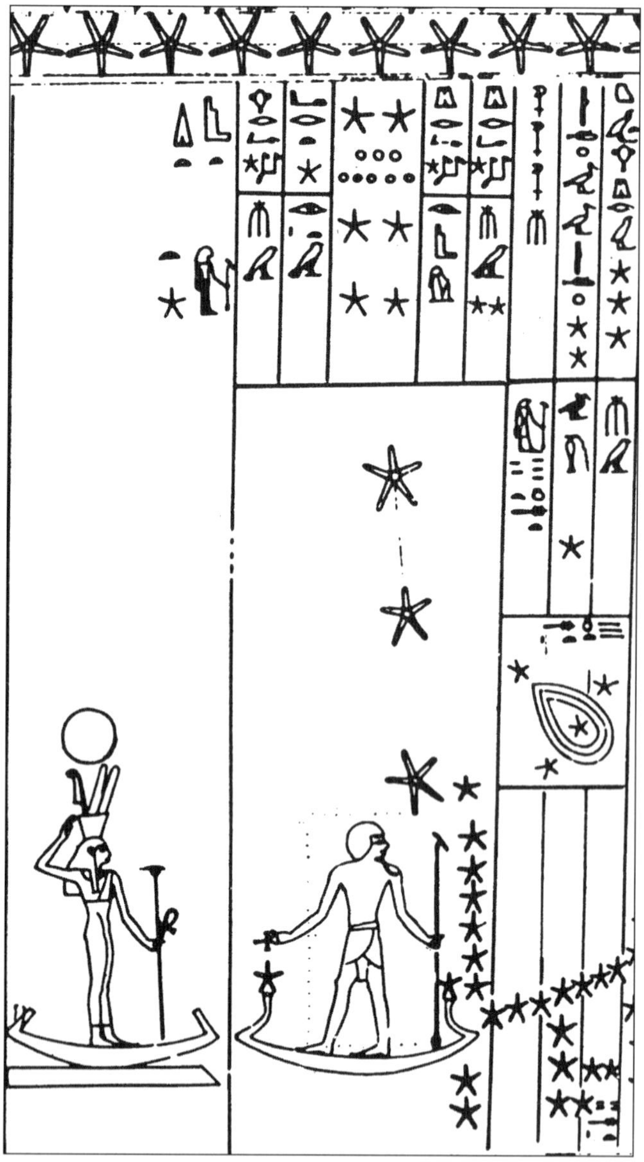

---

[1] O. Neugebauer & R.A. Parker, *EAT* I, Plates 1-23; K. Locher, *JHA* 23, p. 205, Fig. 4.

[2] O. Neugebauer & R.A. Parker, *EAT* III, pp. 113-114.

[3] K. Locher, *New arguments for the celestial location of the decanal belt and for the origin of the s)h-hieroglyph*, VI Congresso internazionale di Egittologia, Atti II, p. 280.

Fig. 15 - Tomb of Senmut, upper register, centre: Sirius and the decans of the Orion group.

the three characteristic stars of the group on Orion's crown, which implies that the Egyptian constellation must have extended considerably further downward[4] (Fig. 17).

[4] The Greeks placed these three stars into the belt of Orion's harness.

Fig. 16 - Sirius and Orion (Sarcophagus Nr 3, Neugebauer & Parker)

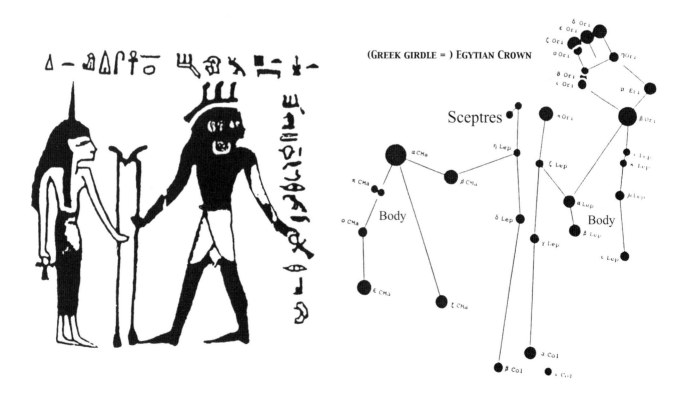

Fig. 17 - Sirius and Orion in the Middle Kingdom. The stars in the Constellation of Orion and the decan *ꜥbwt* (from K. Locher) (Comparison with the image of sarcophagus Nr. 4, Neugebauer-& Parker)

Irrespective of any given period[5], the postures of Sirius and Orion, however, remain the same: both their faces look in the direction of the progression of the decans. Sothis, in the form of Isis, looks at Orion-Osiris moving away; the eyes are turned to where he is going, but the body is twisted back, so that it seems to march towards Isis. In the image in the Ramesseum[6], this impression is reinforced still further by the fact that the two barques very clearly face each other (Fig. 18).

The torsion of Osiris' body and the two boats facing each other clearly indicate that there is a break, the passage from one cycle to another: thus, the two solar boats, day and night, evoking the cycle of the day[7], are always shown prow to prow. In this instance, the point of rupture separates two annual cycles. Facing Sirius, Orion looking behind, proclaims the end of the preceding year and Isis-Sirius inaugurates the new one[8].

---

[5] Further images in H. Brugsch, Thesaurus, p. 80

[6] This is the picture which, by its precision of detail, provides the best information.

[7] E. Thomas, *JEA* 42, pp. 65-79.

[8] As early as the texts of the Pyramids, Orion marking the end of the year is assimilated with Osiris, and Sirius, indicating the new year, as she who gives new life.

Fig. 18 - Ceiling of the Ramesseum. Upper register, central section. The two boats facing each other define the limits of the cycles.

Fig. 19 - Sirius and Orion, sarcophagus of Idy
(Photo University of Tübingen)

Fig. 20 - Sirius and Orion, Sirius in the form of a cow,
Dendera: Ceiling of the entrance to the hypostyle, detail. (Photo K. Locher)

2. Sirius and the sothic year

2.1 Definition of the sothic year and explanation of the heliacal rise

The sothic year is the lapse of time which passes between two heliacal rises of Sirius, at the same latitude[1] of reference. The heliacal rise of a star is its once-a-year reappearance, after a period of absence from the visible sky. The heliacal rise concerned here is, of course, **the visible one**, i.e. the one which the Egyptians could observe. For astronomers, a heliacal rise is the conjunction of the sun and a star, or at least their simultaneous appearance on the horizon. The true heliacal rise of the astronomers is precisely calculable, but cannot be observed because the sun's radiance dazzles the observer and thus renders the star invisible. The visible rise occurs slightly later, when the Earth has moved further on her orbit and the star can be seen a little earlier at the end of the night, before the sun rises. This time lapse between true and visible rise is bigger, the weaker the star's own light or radiance. The angle between the star on its first appearance before dawn and the sun defines its angle of visibility or *arcus visionis*: about 11° for brilliant stars, 14° for lesser ones. For the extremely brilliant Sirius, that angle is noticeably smaller (~ 9°), which is an essential factor.

In Egyptian, the reappearance of Sirius is termed "exit of Sirius" – in the sense of "coming out" – (*prt špdt*). The position of the Earth on its movement around the sun determines whether a star can be seen or not, and its heliacal rise, which varies according to the individual position of each star (Fig. 21).

In order to understand the diagram in Fig. 21, it is important to note that **only those stars are visible which face the dark, nightly part of the hemisphere**[2].

The diagram is simplified insofar as it places the stars on the level of the ecliptic. This is done to explain why a heliacal rise takes place at the end of the night, and why it is linked to the seasons.

a - Heliacal rises are a phenomenon of the night's end

Due to the sense of the Earth's advance along its orbit and to its rotation around its axis, the reappearance or heliacal rise of a star invariably happens just before dawn, i.e. in the 12th hour of the night for the Egyptians. From the day of heliacal rise, any given star becomes visible ever earlier during the night as the Earth moves along her orbit; the star is only visible in the earliest part of the night and then ends up by vanishing altogether once more. This schedule is the same for the 36 stars figuring on the diagram, but, of course, for each one at different times of the year. Thus the various decanal stars rise and disappear successively in the course of one year.

b - Heliacal rises are linked to the season

One and the same star becomes visible each year only when the Earth reaches the same point on her orbit. This is the reason for the relationship between the appearance of a given star and the seasons, which in turn depend on the position of the Earth in relation to the sun. For Sirius, the heliacal rise happens in summer, when the northern hemisphere is turned towards the sun. As it is the summer monsoons in Ethiopia which are largely responsible for the flooding of the Nile, the coincidence between the reappearance of Sirius and the beginning of the Nile flooding is explained[3].

---

[1] The question of the latitude of reference will be discussed infra.

[2] On the cenotaph of Seti I in Abydos we find the phrase (in a second tense): *"it is only at night that these stars navigate across the sky on its exterior"*, O. Neugebauer & R.A. Parker, *EAT* I, Plate 51 (Dramatic text line 1).

[3] The heliacal rise of Sirius coincided with the summer solstice in around 3000 B.C. Currently, the rise happens, for the same latitude, almost 1½ months after the solstice.

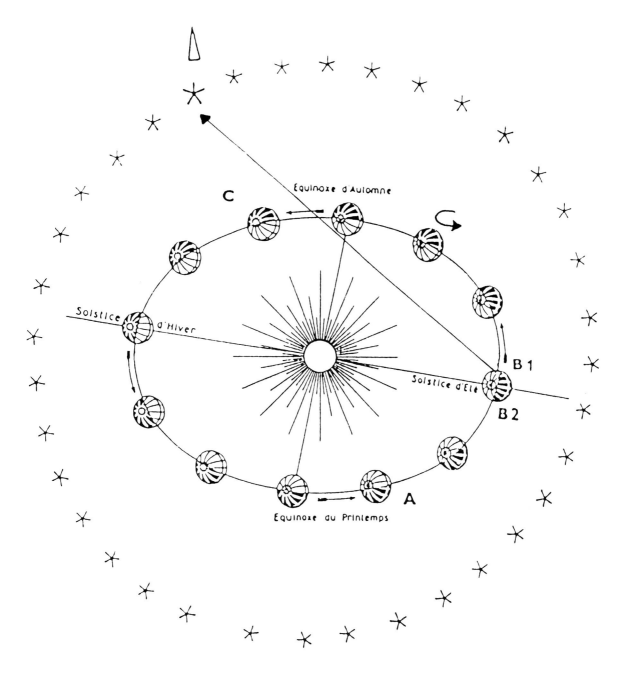

Fig. 21 - Heliacal rise of Sirius and the 36 decanal stars;
visibility and absence of the stars during the year

The figure shows the Earth's yearly orbit around the sun. The anti-clockwise path is indicated by the straight arrow (→). At it follows its yearly orbit, the Earth also turns around its own axis, which creates the day (the hemisphere facing the sun) and night (opposite hemisphere). The curved arrow (↻) shows the sense of rotation. The biggest star is Sirius (△).

The Earth is in A: Only the stars facing the dark, nightly hemisphere are visible. Sirius cannot be seen, the sun prevents it. This is its period of invisibility.

The Earth is in B: The observer in **B1** (end of the night) will perceive Sirius just before dawn: this is the visible heliacal rise of the star. The observer in **B2** (beginning of the night) cannot see it, still hidden by the Earth; he can only see it some hours later, when he has reached **B1** due to the Earth's rotation.

The Earth is in C: Sirius is visible throughout the night.

2.2 Duration of the sothic year

Irrespective of whether the "astronomical" or the "observable" heliacal rise are taken as reference, the length of the sothic year remains the same. It is noticeably shorter than that of the other stars, due to its position and proper movement. Its duration is of 365.2500 mean days[4], whereas other stars, on average, have a mean interval of 365.2563 days between two heliacal rises.

Considering this time between two heliacal rises for various stars, Sirius becomes evidently by far the most interesting, because its duration comes closest to the solar, tropical year[5], which seems to be the most obvious reason for its choice. But this choice of Sirius as a marker for the beginning of the year offers two further advantages: thanks to the duration of **exactly 365¹/₄** days, for one, the entire system can easily be compiled into entire days; and secondly, a particular calendar can be structured on this basis.

a - The full number of entire days

One of the most obvious and major difficulties of the elaboration of a calendar lies in the fact that astronomical cycles do not add up to full numbers of days. The tropical solar year, for instance, with its length of 365.242192643 days, rounded up to 365.2422, complicates the creation of a solar calendar. It could certainly function for some time, but will never be perfectly exact over long periods, because the fractions of days accrue, ending up in sizeable discrepancies. **If, on the other hand, the count of years is carried out in terms of sothic**[6] **and not solar years, the problem of the fractions is totally eliminated. One full day is simply added every fourth year to stay perfectly in phase with the astronomical phenomenon of the heliacal rise** which takes place again after exactly 365¹/₄ days. Counting years in terms of sothic years therefore remains much more precise over very long periods than to do so in terms of natural or solar years.

It is on the basis of the way and method of counting the additional day every fourth year that the entire calendaric system is developed.

b - The quadriennal additional day.

If the Sothis-Sirius year lasts 365¹/₄ days, it obviously creates an additional day every four years, i.e. a quadriennal sixth epagomene. The fact that we have no written confirmation concerning this sixth epagomene which should, in all logic, be added every four years to the fixed year, could easily be attributed to the fragmentary character of the documentation of which we dispose. What is much more intriguing, however, is that Greek texts repeatedly insist on the fact that **no day was ever added at all**. As an example, Diodorus Siculus[7] relates that:

"...the Egyptians organise months and years in a very special way. Relating the days not to the movement of the moon but of the sun, they count

---

4 The duration of the sothic year is, in fact, very slowly increasing. It has been calculated for E. Meyer (*Chronologie Egyptienne*, transl. Moret, pp. 15-16) by Prof. Förster, with the use of the ancient Oppolzer tables. The figures in R. Weill, *Chronologie Egyptienne*, p. 25 are:
   in 4231 B. C.   365.2498352 days
   in 3231   "   365.2500000   "
   in 2231   "   365.2502901   "
   in 1231   "   365.2505225   "
   in 231   "   365.2508804   "
   in 770 A.D.   365.2513026   " . The increase between 4000 B.C. and 770 A.D. was 0.0015 days.
   M.F. Ingham, *JEA* 55, p. 40, finds similar values, barely superior for an arc of vision a little lower than that of the direct observation carried out by L. Borchardt in 1925:
   in 3498 B.C.   365.25051 days
   in 2043   "   365.25085   "
   in 590   "   365.25126   "
   in 861 A. D.   365.25181   " , where the increase does not go beyond 0.0018 days. **For the entire duration of the history of Egypt, one can therefore admit a figure of 365¹/₄ days for the sothic year.**
5 Rounded up to 365.2422 days; the displacement of the seasons is almost one month in 120 years in the mobile year, but is reduced to 1 day every 129 years in the fixed sothic year.
6 Egyptian texts state that the years are counted as sothic years. One can read at Dendera *"...the years are counted according to his (=Sothis') rise"*, H. Brugsch, *Thesaurus*, p. 100.
7 Diodorus Siculus, I., L.

*months of 30 days, and after each 12th month, they interpose 5¹/₄ days; in this way, they complete the duration of the annual turn. They do not, by the way, add intercalary months, **nor introduce days**, as is frequently done by the Greeks."*

What is particularly noticeable in this passage is the coexistence side by side of two affirmations which seem contradictory: on the one hand, Diodorus confirms the existence of a fixed year of 365¹/₄ days, but on the other hand he denies the use of an intercalary day.

In the same train of thought, some terms and expressions in the Decree of Canopus may appear strange under closer scrutiny. Promulgated in the year 9 of Ptolemy III Euergetes, he plans to fix the mobile year, whose inconveniences are detailed in some length:

"...in order to have the seasons follow an absolute rule[8], that the days of certain solemn feasts to celebrate in winter should never fall into summer[9] because of the displacement of the rise of Sothis by one day every 4 years, and so that other feasts among those now celebrated in summer shall not be celebrated in winter in times to come, as has already happened and will happen again..."

The decree then proposed to add a sixth epagomene:

"...Henceforth, a day shall be added[10]...every fourth year to the five epagomenoi before the New Year...".

The rise of Sirius, however, is maintained as the inaugural point of the year:

"...on the day when rises the star of Isis, the

day recognised by the scriptures of the House of Life as being the New Year[11]..."

One perceives, of course, the usefulness of replacing the vague year with a fixed one. But if the heliacal rise of the star is to indicate the new year in the same way as before, as stipulated in "the writings of the House of Life", then the Decree simply creates a year of 365¹/₄ days... which already existed, since that is the exact time between two heliacal rises of Sirius. How then, is the phrase to be explained:

"...henceforth, a day shall be added... every fourth year..." ?

How then, is the well-attested use of the sothic year of 365¹/₄ days, reconfirmed by the very terms of the Decree, to be reconciled with the need to specify that henceforth a sixth epagomene shall be added to fix the year?

One is forcibly led to the hypothesis that the additional day generated every 4 years by the sothic year **was not actually added** as a quadriennal intercalary day. The only way to account for this additional ¹/₄ day, then, would be to use both years at the same time. The sothic and the mobile year would simply glide one against the other by a day every four years. **The advance of the rise of Sirius by one day every four years in the vague year would thus not be a simple incidence – as believed so far – of the difference in length between the sothic year (365¹/₄ days) and the mobile one (365 days). It is, quite on the contrary, the means – and in fact the only possible means – to count the additional day without ever having to add an intercalary one.** In this way, the Sothis years of 365 ¹/₄ days can be counted with precision, all the while using the year of 365 full days.

If we admit that the gliding of the day of Sirius' heliacal rise every fourth year within the mobile year is not an epiphenomenon but the result of a well-thought out decision, we can then accept that there is not a fixed year on the one hand and a mobile year on the other – each one progressing

---

[8] Decree of Canopus (Line 20 of the hieroglyphic text).

[9] Decree of Canopus (Line 21 of the hieroglyphic text). The passage confirms that the feasts moved, as Geminus had already written in his treatise on astronomy (see Letronne, Nouvelles recherches, pp. 9-10). The relationship between the movement of feast days and that of the rise of the star will again be examined infra.

[10] Decree of Canopus (Line 22 of the hieroglyphic text). The term is *wȝḥ*, the same word is used for the 5 days added to the year.

[11] Decree of Canopus (Line 18 of the hieroglyphic text).

independently – but a **coupled mechanism** in which either is indispensable, and in which both are tied together indissolubly, producing a kind of **gliding calendar** whose ultimate direct expression is the Grand Period of 1460 years[12] (to be discussed in more detail on p. 40). In other words: to make the system work, the **mobile year becomes an absolute necessity**.

Under this premise things fall into place, the entire subject becomes logical and coherent: the otherwise inexplicable Egyptian attachment to their mobile year and its perennity[13], and the affirmation found in the writings of all the ancient authors that *"no day was introduced"*[14]. And as regards the mandatory oath which the Pharaohs were said to have sworn in the temple of Isis (as Sirius is represented): to respect the year by *"...continuing to count 365..."* and never to intercalate *"...neither a month, nor a day... as it had been fixed by the Ancients..."*, this oath now takes on its full meaning and importance, and could furthermore bear witness to the very ancient origin of the system.

J.A. Letronne perceived the relationship between the sothic period and its four-year span of gliding: *"This canicular period (Sirius = dog star = stella caniculae) of 4 years which suggests a fixed year of 365¹/₄ days, shows a remarkable symmetry with the great canicular period. It is, in fact, composed of 4 years of 365, i.e. 1460 days, to which a day was added, making 1461 days. The great period, which brought the first day of Thôt back to the heliacal rise, was composed of 4 x 365, i.e. 1460 years, to which a year was added, making 1461. The two periods thus calculate in the same way, the small one in days, the big one in years:*
in one: 4 years of 365 days = 1460 days,
in the other: 4 x 365 years = 1460 years, with the smaller one contained 365 times in the big one"[15].

Intuitively, he concludes: *"These two periods seem to be inseparable, everything pointing to the idea that they are part of a system which was conceived in a single effort. Both periods must date from the same epoch and must have been established at the same time..."*.

He does not, however, conclude that the link between them was precisely the gliding of the intercalary day. He writes a little further (p. 65 of the same book): *"Nothing indicates, however, how this intercalation was done; yet one can undoubtedly presume that it was not carried out by the addition of a sixth epagomene after four years, which was the only way of intercalation which the regularity of the Egyptian months would allow".*

This gliding of the fixed and mobile year against each other is not just a neat subterfuge either; it is the very cornerstone of the entire edifice, the key to the creation of the calendar. It is of considerable importance on a structural level (the functioning mechanism of the calendar) and even more so on the conceptual level (the long-term vision and the evolution of the calendaric organisation in time).

---

[15] J.A. Letronne, (Nouvelles Recherches, p. 54).

---

[12] As the heliacal rise glides by a day every fourth year, it runs through the entire mobile year in 1460 years, i.e. one sothic period.

[13] The mobile years continue through the entire history of Egypt. The reform proposed in the Decree of Canopus was never implemented.

[14] With this, the terms of the Decree of Canopus become much clearer: its purpose was not so much to introduce a fixed year, which was already well known, but above all to break the link between the mobile and the fixed year by actually introducing the intercalary day.

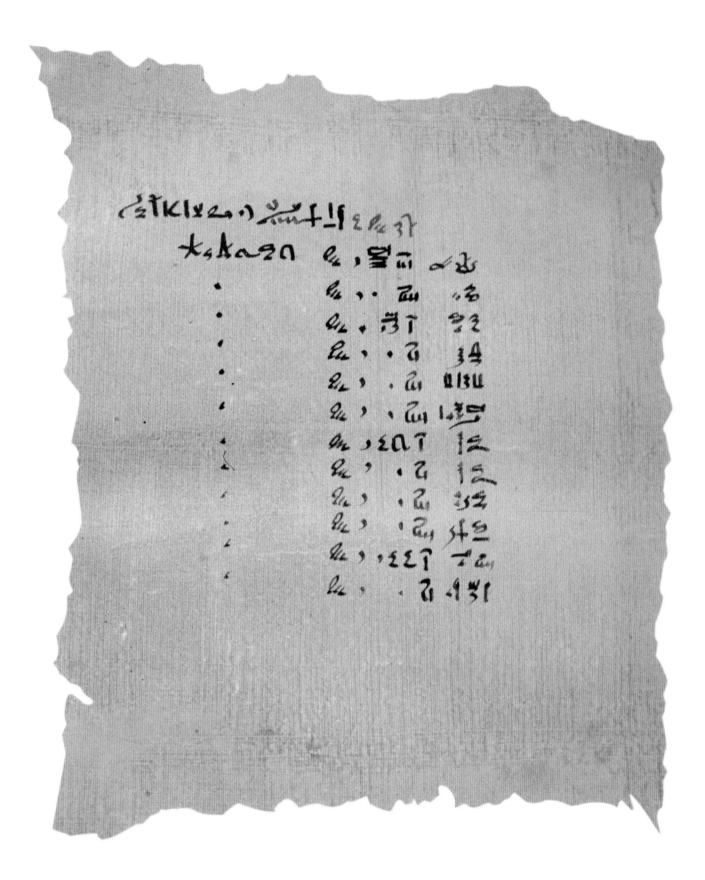

Fig. 22 - Calendar on the reverse side of the Ebers Papyrus (Facsimile from G. Ebers, photo Y. Beaufranc).

3. The concept

3.1 The structural aspect:

The mechanism of the gliding calendar

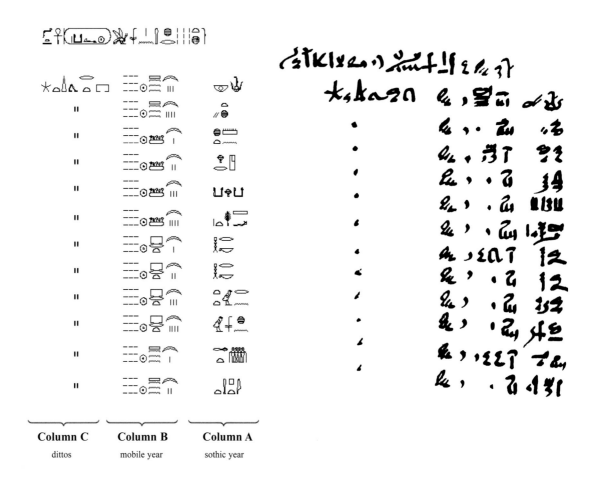

| | Column C | Column B | Column A |
| | dittos | mobile year | sothic year |

Fig. 23 - The Ebers calendar, relative position of the fixed and the mobile year.

Gliding and relative position of the fixed and mobile year (near the end of a sothic period)
Column A: the fixed calendar and the feast days in the sothic year
Column B: corresponding days in the then current vague year
Column C: the ditto signs

A document which seemingly shows the fixed and mobile year in parallel, provides some suggestions about how the system functioned. On the reverse side of a great medical papyrus called Papyrus Ebers[1], a calendar can be found which gives a sothic date[2] as well as a list of feast days relating to the mobile year (Fig. 22, 23).

One can read:

In the year 9 of the majesty of the King of Upper and Lower Egypt Djeser-ka-Rê[3], living forever

Wpt-rnpt	(feast of New Year)	3rd mth of Summer	day 9	Exit of Sirius
Tḫ	(name of 1st mth)	4th mth of Summer	day 9	"
Mnḫt	(name of 2nd mth)	1st mth of Flood,	day 9	"
Ḥt-ḥr	(Hathor, 3rd mth)	2nd mth of Flood,	day 9	"
K3-ḥr-k3	(name of 4th mth)	3rd mth of Flood,	day 9	"
Šfbdt	(name of 5th mth)	4th mth of Flood,	day 9	"
Rkḥ [wr]	(name of 6th mth)	1st mth of Winter,	day 9	"
Rkḥ [wr]	(name of 7th mth)	2nd mth of Winter,	day 9	"
Ḫnsw	(name of 8th mth)	3rd mth of Winter,	day 9	"
Ỉpt-ḥmt	(Khonsou, 9th mth)	4th mth of Winter,	day 9	"
Ḫnty-ḫty	(name of 10th mth)	1st mth of Summer	day 9	"
Ỉpt-ḥmt	(name of 11th mth)	2nd mth of Summer	day 9	"

Column A   **Column B**   **Column C**

[1] Publication by A. Eisenlohr, *ZÄS* 8, pp. 165-166, and G. Ebers, *Papyros Ebers*, Vol. 1, Plate 1 (reproduction of facsimile courtesy of the University of Leipzig). For the history of interpretations and bibliography on this document see Ch. Leitz, *Studien zur ägyptischen Astronomie*, pp. 28-34, and ibid. note 25, p. 29; L. Depuydt, *Orientalia* 65, pp. 86-88.

[2] Only the structure of the calendar is evoked in this context, and not its dating. For dating purposes, see E. Hornung, *Untersuchungen zur Chronologie und Geschichte des Neuen Reiches*, Ägyptologische Abhandlungen 11, pp. 15-23.

[3] The king's name, read as Djeser-ka-Rê, was declared to be Amenhotep I, 2nd king in the 18th dynasty.

This is the only known manuscript to provide an entire year's list of the monthly feast days in the sothic calendar, with their equivalents in the mobile one.

The data are presented in 3 columns, which are spaced more widely separated in this transcription and translation, to allow for clearer distinction (Fig. 23):

Column A presents a list of feast days 30 days apart. The first one is the feast of the celebration of the rise of Sirius and is thus the sothic column.

Column B shows the dates as they normally appear in the mobile year: to each feast day in the fixed year corresponds a mobile date[4], the first one being the famous "sothic date" indicating the day of the rising star in the vague year. Like a snapshot, the gliding movement is immobilised and fixed at a precise point of one sothic period – i.e. within 1460 years[5].

Column C simply shows an assembly of dittos under the mention of Sirius' rise.

Each of the columns presents its own problems of interpretation, but also has certain elements which spotlight the mechanism of the gliding calendar.

1 - Column A - The problem of the month's name

The column is split into 12 portions of 30 days, according to the feast days, as in the representations on the Karnak water clock or in the Ramesseum, where the names of the feast days are put into the third register (Fig. 12, 13). We know that these feasts give their names to the months, but the one at the beginning of the year holds the place of the 12th month of the graeco-roman order, which

appears like a displacement of one month[6] in comparison to the normal lists.

The Egyptians consider the first appearance of Sirius, before the sun rises, as the 12th hour of the night preceding New Year's Day[7]; strictly speaking, that would still be in the preceding year, marking its very end. Curiously, **the Ebers calendar does not mention the 5 epagomene days**, and the names of feasts seem to glide along the months of the mobile year without taking any account of them. If we accept that the rise of Sirius takes place at the limit[8] between the 12th month of the ending year and the 1st month of the following year, *wp rnpt* then becomes the name of the 12th month, marking its end as the eponymic feast. The following feast *Tḥ* marks the end of the first month, 30 days later, and the feasts of the fixed calendar[9] following that of the rise of Sirius, in this way separate the year into 12 "months", **indicating their end and not their beginning**. Consequently, the discrepancy with the graeco-roman order of things is not of a month, but merely of one hour in relation to the sothic, and of 5 days in relation to the mobile year, as we shall see. This difference is, of course, attributable to the epagomenoi.

---

[6] R. Krauss, *Sothis und Monddaten*, p. 105 ff. Concerning the names of the months, and particularly that of the 12th month see A. Gardiner, *ZÄS* 43, pp. 136-144 and *RdE* 10, pp. 9-31; R.A. Parker, *Calendars*, p. 31 and *RdE* 11, pp. 85-107; J. von Beckerath, *ZÄS* 120, pp. 17-21 and pp. 131-136; L. Depuydt, *Civil Calendar and Lunar Calendar*, pp. 217 à 248.

[7] To state that the New Year begins with the appearance of Sirius would imply that it began before sunrise. Concerning the beginning of days see J.von Beckerath, *ZÄS* 120, 1993, p. 21 and R. Krauss, *BSEG* 14, pp. 54-56. For A. Spalinger in *ZÄS* 119, p. 155, *ḥd-t3* is the exact limit between night and day, i.e. the passage from the 12th hour of night into the 1st hour of day.

[8] This is the simplest explanation of the name of the 12th month, *wpt-rnpt* as equivalent of Mesore. There is no need for the intervention of any lunar month; A. Spalinger, *BES* 10, pp. 139-140, also contests the lunar character of the Ebers calendar.

[9] During the entire long period in which the gliding calendar worked, the use of the month names of the fixed year was probably avoided for the dates of the mobile year, in order to avoid any possible confusion. This is why the months are merely designated by their number in the season.

---

[4] This is indeed the day of the feast, relating to a day in the mobile year.

[5] These dates must be understood as give or take four years, because the rise of Sirius stays within the same day for 4 vague years.

2 - Column B - The place of the epagomenoi

In column B, the epagomenoi do not appear after the 30th day of the 4th month *šmw*, and the total number of days seems to be 360 in both columns. The cycle of Sothis-Sirius of 1460 years, however, with its passage of the rise of Sothis through each day of the vague year, of which the document shows an example, imposes the use of the epagomenoi[10]. The five days "added to the year" of column A can only be placed in one single position: they must be put after the 9th day of the 3rd month *šmw* of the following mobile year, but counted **outside the year**, just before the next rise of Sirius[11]; thus they are counted at the end of the fixed year[12], as the gliding system functions, in order to maintain the regular sothic cycle of the Great Year. **In conclusion, in the fixed as well as in the mobile year the epagomenoi are always placed at the end of the year but counted outside of it**, having a position out of step in both years[13]. Their respective position migrates due to the gliding mechanism between the two types of years, one against the other[14]. One immediately perceives the important implications of this interpretation for chronology: the epagomenoi of the sothic column, when they relate to a day in the vague year, have the same chronological value as that of the rise, i.e. they define a date precisely, give or take 1460 years[15].

The fact that the five epagomenoi do not appear in the Ebers calendar draws attention to two points of capital importance:
- the determination of the monthly feast days,
- the decanal structure of both the mobile and the fixed year.

a - Determination of the monthly feast days

The Ebers calendar (Fig. 23) shows that the interval of the feasts of the fixed year of 30 days does not take any account of the epagomenoi of the mobile year.

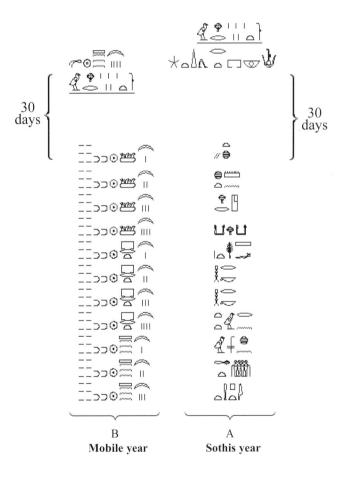

Fig. 24 - Presumed relative situation of the fixed and the mobile year when the calendar of monthly feast days was established.

---

[10] No author appears to contest the value of the sothic date of the document. In all logic, one cannot on one hand accept the sothic dating and on the other qualify the document as virtual or without any astronomic value in its structure because the epagomenoi are absent.

[11] A rise which will still take place on day 9 of the 3rd month *šmw* if in a four-year span, or on day 10 of the same month if it is the following four-year period.

[12] The Dendera texts allude to the birth of Isis at the beginning of the year *nfr* (= fixed), in the night of "the child in its nest" (name of the 5th epagomene). They do not refer to some kind of "ideal" calendar or to the end of a sothic cycle, but clearly to **a reality which repeats itself each year within the fixed year**. (References: H. Brugsch, *Thesaurus*, p. 103; Ch. Leitz, *Studien zur ägyptischen Astronomie*, p. 4, Notes 18-19 and *ZÄS* 120, pp. 139-148; see also A. Spalinger; *JNES* 54, pp. 40-42 and p. 44 concerning the confusion between the 4th and 5th epagomene).

[13] This would seem to be the opinion of A. Spalinger, *BES* 10, p. 140, Note 11.

[14] This discrepancy could explain certain anomalies and account for their presence or absence in the documents, **depending on whether the fixed or the mobile year is taken into account**.

[15] Same as, incidentally, a feast date of the fixed year related to the mobile, as is the case in this document. In fact, each of the horizontal lines in the Ebers calendar must confirm the sothic date by indicating the mobile date of each feast of the fixed calendar.

If the movement is reversed so that both years of the Ebers calendar move back in time until the rise of Sirius coincides with the last hour of the mobile year, this will presumably reveal the original set-up of the calendar of the monthly feast days. They are always separated from each other by 30 days, but with a discrepancy of five days between the fixed and mobile years (Fig. 24).

In column A, each feast of the **fixed year** is placed at the end of the night preceding the first day of the following month[16]. In column B of the **mobile year**, the feast takes place 5 days earlier, within the last 10-day period of the month[17]. **The rise of Sirius takes place in the 5th epagomene in the fixed year, but it is placed in the last day of the 4th month of** *šmw* **in the mobile year**[18], and gives its name to that 12th month. Like all others, this 12th month bears the name of its closing feast, i.e. *wpt-rnpt*: opening of the year, or mesore: birth of the sun[19]. This gap in feast

days between fixed and mobile year in the Ebers papyrus presumably points at a concomitance between the setting of the monthly feast dates and the parallel setting of the two years. As the Ebers calendar is written towards the end of a sothic period of 1460 years, this determination of the parallel setting must go back at least to the beginning of that same sothic period.

b - Decanal structure of the fixed and mobile year

The Egyptian year appears to be organised according to the decans much more than to the moon. Admittedly, the division into 12 units of 30 days obviously takes account of the lunar cycles[20]. But the very definition of the 5 days called "in addition" to the year of 360 days, or "outside" the year, is the strongest possible argument in favour of a decanal structure[21]. The five epagomenoi are by no means an appendix added later on to some primitive compilation, but are much more probably part of the initial creation of the calendar, and a witness to its decanal structure. In the astronomical representations like those in the Ramesseum (Fig. 13) the decans are shown to follow Sirius, whereas those of the epagomenoi are set apart, together with the planets.

3 - Column C - The ditto signs

In the third column (Fig. 23), ditto signs are traced each month under the term "exit of Sirius". If we assume that they refer to the text above them (vertical interpretation), the sign would represent "appearance of Sirius", and it must be envisaged that the calendar shows the sequence of almost an entire sothic cycle from the 9th day of the 3rd month *šmw* on. The date at the beginning, "year 9 of the King", however, does not encourage this interpretation but indicates, rather, that the table is valid for that year 9 only. Consequently, the interpretation by Leitz[22] (horizontal interpretation) becomes the most logical one. In this, the ditto signs

---

[16] Hence the feast calendars setting *Tḥ* at the first day of the 2nd month of *3ḥt* and so on for all the feast days.

[17] The feast days of column B remain tied to the mobile year which they follow through the seasons, and most documents indicate these dates in the civil year. They are set in the last decade of the month, some on the 26th day, others a little later (*Rnnt* on the 28th), still others earlier (*Tḥ* on the 20th). About this last feast, see A. Spalinger, *SAK* 20, pp. 289-303. The Ebers calendar clearly shows that there does indeed exist a feast calendar in the fixed year in addition to the mobile. R.A. Parker, *Calendars*, p. 39, also thought that there existed a double feast calendar. See also U. Luft, *Die chronologische Fixierung des ägyptischen Mittleren Reiches nach dem Tempelarchiv von Illahun*, p. 215 ff., and *The Date of the w3gy Feast: Considerations on the Chronology of the Old Kingdom*, in: Revolutions in Time, Studies in Ancient Egyptian Calendrics, pp. 39-44.
From the terms of the Decree of Canopus, which points at moving the rise of Sirius as the reason for the movement of the feast days in the mobile year (line 21), it must in all logic follow that the installation of the feast calendar was originally determined by the day of heliacal rise of that star.

[18] In the Leyden papyrus, T 32, IV, 2-3 we find: *"... Your years are millions, incessantly, eternally, the 4th (month) of šmw, the day of the appearance of Sirius, mistress of the beginning of the year"*; see F.R. Herbin, *"Le livre de Parcourir l'Eternité"*, OLA 58, p. 56 and 443 with Plate IV. This sentence in a way resumes the theory of the Gliding Calendar by demonstrating that on the one hand the years are counted in sothic years (Sirius marking their beginning), but also that these sothic years are usually related to the civil or mobile year (the rise being dated on the last day of *šmw* and not on the 5th epagomene).

[19] For R.A. Wells, *SAK* 19, p. 313, the name of Mesore is derived from the fact that the winter solstice originally fell into this month. But it could well allude to the phenomenon of the heliacal rise, i.e. to the almost simultaneous rise of Sirius and the sun.

---

[20] See the chapter on the moon.

[21] The year of 360 days is a logical consequence of the definition of the decan, see the relevant chapter.

[22] Ch. Leitz, *Studien zur ägyptischen Astronomie*, p. 28.

avoid having to re-state, after the date of the vague year, the name of each feast already stated on the same line for the fixed year. Thus, under "exit of Sirius", one should read, successively, *Tḥ*, *Mnḫt*, etc...

It remains to evaluate the purpose of this calendar and the reason for its writing. On this papyrus it may even have been the coincidences in the figures, all multiples of 3, which struck the writer[23]: in the year 9, the rise took place on day 9 of the 3rd month of the 3rd season and due to the 30 days interval between the feasts of the fixed calendar, they would all correspond to the day 9 of the civil calendar.

3.2 The conceptual aspect: evolution in time

The principal qualities of a calendar are first, of course, simplicity, which renders it easy to use. But second, and above all else, it must be reliable over long periods of time, otherwise its organisation would require constant review.

Comparing the evolution over a long period of time between the Julian[24] year and the coupled sothic and mobile years will reveal a clearer picture of the profound reasons which may have motivated the

choice of the sothic in preference to the solar[25] year, as well as the gliding by one day every fourth year rather than the insertion of a sixth epagomene.

The sothis year and the Julian year have exactly the same duration of 365¼ days. **The Julian year, however, has this duration by definition, whereas the sothic has the advantage of astronomical determination.** The Julian year counts each fourth year as a bissextile one, adding an intercalary day, whereas in the sothic-mobile couple, that day is skipped by the gliding.

Considering the course of the sun, e.g. the wandering of the spring equinox, it will obviously be the same in both models because they have the same duration, both being longer than the natural tropical year. The spring equinox will therefore advance by 0.0078 days[26] each year, representing a discrepancy of one day in 129 years, both in the sothic and the Julian years. **But the evolution over this long time will turn out to be very different in the two models:**

a - In the Julian system,

as the intercalary days are added, the excess fraction of 0.0078 days p.a. accumulates over the years to form entire days. In A.D. 1582, the dislocation caused by the Julian calendar became too important: spring, announced by its equinox, came 11 days early, which provoked the Gregorian calendar reform[27].

---

[23] The Egyptians seemed to attach quite some importance to coincidences. Overleaf of the Rhind Mathematical Papyrus (Peet, *The Rhind Mathematical Papyrus*, pp. 129-131, Nr. 87 and plate Y) one can find for the year 11 of an unidentified king: "First month of *3ḫt*, day 3: birth of Seth (3rd epagomene), it has thundered; Birth of Isis (4th epagomene), it has rained". Note that the 3rd and 4th epagomenoi are related to a single day in the mobile year, for they must be counted outside the year in the same way as in the Ebers papyrus. This parallel setting of epagomenoi with the beginning of the first season could indicate that the date noted in the Rhind papyrus is close to the beginning of a sothic period.

[24] The Julian Year was installed in 45 B.C. by Julius Caesar. We do not take into account its internal structure in this context, but merely its duration of 365¼ days by definition, with one intercalary day added after four years.

[25] Another inconvenience of the true solar year for the count of years is that it is never easy to determine precisely the point of departure, equinox or solstice, because of the very gradual and progressive reduction or increase in length of the days and nights. The beginning of the sothic year, on the contrary, has a clear, easily observable marker; its lateness by one day every fourth year in the mobile year is no mathematical artifice, but is clearly marked by a well-defined astronomical event: the yearly date in the mobile year of the rise of Sirius, which allows to count the years easily and precisely.

[26] This is the difference between the 365.2500 days of the sothic and Julian years, and the 365.2422 days of the tropical year.

[27] The reform was carried out under Pope Gregory XIII Boncompagni, following the concept of Luigi Lilio. The equinox is set back in its proper place by cancelling out 10 days. The Julian calendar continues, but with the following modifications allowing to adhere as closely as possible to the length of the solar year: 3 leap years are cancelled over 400 years by declaring that the secular years are only bissextile if divisible by 400 (whereas all secular years were bissextile in the Julian calendar). This results in a duration of 365.2425 days for the Gegorian year, which amounts to merely one excess day in 3000 years. Again, however, the error is cumulative.

b - In the system of the sothic-mobile couple

we also end up with 11 days displacement within a sothic period[28]. But as the mobile-sothic couple is a circular system, the gliding continues until, another 47 years later, i.e. after 1507 years[29], the spring equinox will very naturally have returned to the same day of the mobile year as 1507 years before.

JULIAN YEAR	SOTHIC/MOBILE COUPLE
DURATION 365¼ days **by definition**	**DURATION** 365¼ days between 2 heliacal rises of Sirius with **astronomical landmark**
NO GLIDING **quadriennal addition of intercalary days** The excess fractions of 0.0078 days p.a. accumulate. ⟶	**GLIDING** **quadriennal additional days are skipped by the gliding movement in the mobile year.** The excess fractions of 0.0078 days p.a. follow the gliding movement. ⟲
LINEAR SYSTEM REQUIRING CORRECTIONS	CYCLICAL SYSTEM WITH PERIODICALLY RECURRING AUTO-REGULATION

Fig. 25 - Comparison of the long term evolution of the Julian year and the sothic-mobile couple.

The choice of Sirius as the marker indicating the beginning of the year thus appears as singularly astute:

1. its annual reappearance is an *easily observed astronomical event* due to the star's great brilliance and its easily detected position in relation to the constellation of Orion[30],

2. the star's interval between two heliacal rises *is closest to the duration of the tropical year*,

3. due to this interval of *exactly* **365¼** days, i.e. one full day every 4th year, the problem of the fractions of days is eliminated on the one hand, and on the other, *a gliding system* of 4-year intervals of the rise can be created for the very precise count of the years, without the help of added intercalary days,

4. the gliding of the fixed and mobile years, one against the other, **results in an automatic resetting of equinoxes and solstices in the mobile year** after a period of 1507 years, thus avoiding the adjustments which the use of intercalary days would have rendered necessary[31].

---

[28] In 1460 years, the discrepancy between the tropical solar year of 365.2422 days and the sothic year of 365.2500 days amounted to a total of 11.4 days.

[29] As the uncoupling of the same equinox and the same solstice in the mobile year amounts to 0.2422 days p.a., the complete revolution is accomplished in 1507 years (i.e. 365 : 0.2422)

[30] See R.A. Wells, *Re and the Calendars* in Revolutions in Time, p. 12 figure 5.

[31] The system is operational as long as the sothic year lasts 365¼ days, i.e. during the entire length of Egyptian history.

This implies that at the time when the displacement of the seasons (11 days) was resented as insupportable, the Julian system imposed a correction by installing the Gregorian calendar in order to avoid a recurrence. **In the Egyptian system**, at approximately the same point (11 days displacement in the fixed year), **the correction comes automatically in the mobile year**, due to the coupled mechanism, without the need either to remove or to add a single day. **This return into phase with the course of the sun occurs spontaneously and regularly after each cycle of 1507 years**, without the need for any kind of readjustment in time.

The inconvenience of the system is that it imposes the **continued existence of the mobile year** with its corollary of the unavoidable displacement of the seasons in the vague year, which

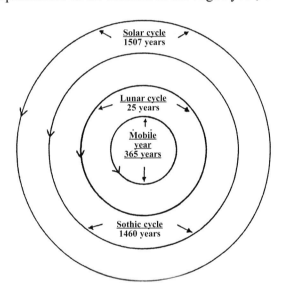

Fig. 26 - The Gliding Calendar. All astronomical cycles glide within the mobile year

reaches a maximum after 753 years. Once installed, however, the gliding system relates all of the astronomical cycles to the number of full days in the mobile year: for any given cycle, the fractions will add up and as they reach a full day, the astronomical phenomenon concerned will simply be observed a day later or earlier in the civil calendar. The system thus establishes an **autoregulation of the cycles** which return automatically into their original place in a simple way, and with a precision – especially over long periods of time – which any linear system with its cumulative imprecisions can never equal.

By the yardstick of the mobile year, each astronomical cycle will return to the same day in that mobile or vague year after its proper and specific duration (Fig. 26).

- The solar cycle
The same equinox or solstice will fall into the same day of the mobile year every 1507 years

- The sothic cycle
The heliacal rise of Sirius will fall into the same day of the mobile year every 1460 years

- The lunar cycle
The Egyptians defined[32] the period after which the same lunar phase falls into the same day of the mobile year as 25 years

Knowledge of the periodicity of these cycles of the mobile year contributes precious assistance to studies of chronology, particularly the sothic period. It would be most interesting, for instance, to identify the date of a solstice or equinox in the mobile year, which would fix the event – more or less 1507 years. If perchance, it corresponded also to a sothic date, the precision would then increase to 46827 years[33], more or less 129 years.

Due to its very concept, **such a calendar would thus not only result in automatic, periodical and precise self-regulation, but it would also remain valid and exact over extremely long periods of time**. Such perennity and precision[34] could well be the real fundamental reasons for the insistence on maintaining the use of the vague year, which allowed the gliding sothic-mobile system to remain operational.

---

[32] The document is a late one: O. Neugebauer, A. Volten, Untersuchungen zur antiken Astronomie IV, *Ein demotischer astronomischer Papyrus (Pap. Carlsberg 9)*, Quellen und Studien zur Geschichte der Mathematik, Abt. B, Vol. 4, pp. 383-406; W Barta, *ZÄS* 106, pp. 1-10.
25 years = 25 x 365 days = 9125 days. 9125 : 29.23059 = 309.0016 = 309 lunar months (of which 9 intercalary ones).

[33] This is the time an equinox or solstice require to run through the entire sothic year (365.25 : 0.0078 = 46827 years).

[34] The two notions have Thoth for symbol.

4. The sothic period

A: The great year and the determination of the beginning of the sothic periods

1 - Before Champollion: early sources

Long before Champollion enabled us to read hieroglyphic texts, the existence of this period of 1460 years which Sirius needs to move through every day of the mobile calendar, was discussed by Greek and Roman writers:

One of the first mentions of the cycle comes from Geminus[1].

Censorinus[2] contributes information of capital importance, indicating that in A.D. 139, the heliacal rise fell on the 1st of Thôt, thus initiating what he called the Great Year[3]. This, of course, immediately defines the absolute dates of the other years in which the sothic rise tallies with the 1st Thôt, i.e. the beginnings of the great sothic period[4]:

    139 A.D.
    1321 B.C.
    2781 B.C.
    4241 B.C.
      etc...

The astronomer Theon[5] writes towards the end of the 4th century A.D., that from Pharaoh Menophres[6] until the beginning of the reign of Diocletian (284 A.D.), 1605 years had passed. Deducting 284, we find indeed the year 1321 B.C., which Theon appears to indicate as the beginning of an era.

2 - Since Champollion: data from the Egyptian texts

In 1865 the Decree of Canopus[7] was discovered. It specified that in the year 9 of Ptolemy III Evergetus (= 238 B.C.), Sirius rose on the 1st day of the 2nd month of *šmw*. Calculating both forward and backward, the following period begins indeed in A.D. 139 and the preceding one in 1321 B.C., more than a thousand years earlier. **This official Egyptian text thus confirms the writings of the early authors**.

Another confirmation, incidentally, is brought by the date of instauration of the Alexandrian calendar[8]. It indicates that in 25 B.C., the heliacal rise of Sirius took place on the 25th day of the 3rd month of *šmw*, confirming the same dates for the beginning and the end of the period.

B: Knowledge of the mobile date of the rise of Sirius is important for chronology

The beginnings of sothic periods being thus determined, it follows that mention of a sothic rise together with a day in the mobile year, would definitely fix that date within one of the great cycles of 1460 years: the sothic dating. Documents containing both the fixed and the mobile date are rare, but extremely precious for considerations of chronology.

1 - Among the oldest[9], two documents on papyri:

---

[1] See chapter VI. pp. 32-34 (Petav. Uranol. 1630 in folio)

[2] Censorinus XXI, 10.

[3] "The Great Year" may be understood either as the sothic cycle of 1460 years, or the sothic 1460-day period of 4 years. In the latter case, the year 139 A.D. would, indeed, be the first year in this 4-year period.

[4] All these dates must be understood within 4 years, the rise remaining in the same day for that long.

[5] See Meyer, *Chronologie*, pp. 36-37 and R. Weill, *Chronologie*, pp. 9-10 and 50-51

[6] Identification of this Pharaoh remains controversial; it could be Ramses I, whose name of the King of Upper and Lower Egypt could fit (see T1, T2, T3 in J. von Beckerath, *Handbuch der ägyptischen Königsnamen*, p. 234).

---

[7] First publication Lepsius, *Das bilingue Dekret von Canopus*. For a bibliographic overview see Spalinger, *Three studies*, p.31, Notes 1 and 2.

[8] For the Alexandrian Calendar see Appendix II. It must be noted that even after that date, the sothic-mobile coupling continued to function, because Censorinus mentions the sothic coincidence of the year 139 A.D.

[9] We do not take here into account the coffins of the 9th and 10th dynasties (see chapter on the decans).

—The Kahun letter

Dating from the Middle Kingdom[10], this letter

This great and lovely stele[12] which was raised by Thutmose III, shows him offering water and wine to a sitting, lion-headed wedjat[13], and gives details of

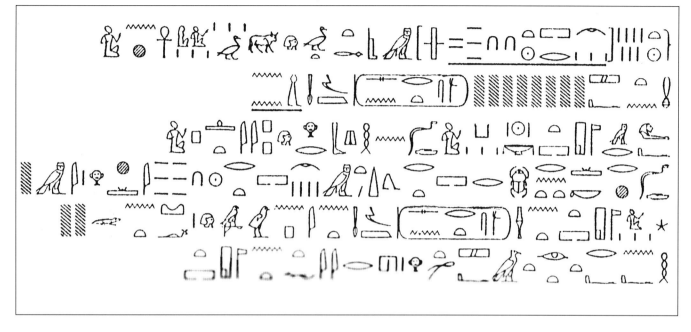

Fig. 27- Kahun letter (from Borchardt)

announces that in the year 7 of Sesostris III, the rise of Sirius will take place on the 16th day of the 4th month of the winter season *prt* (Fig. 27).

— The Ebers Papyrus

This document[11] mentions, as we have seen, a sothic rise on the 9th day of the 3rd month of *šmw*, in the 9th year of a king whose name has been read as Djeserkare, and who has been identified as Amenhotep I, second king of the 18th dynasty (see Fig. 22 and 23). However, the sign ⌒ in his name can be read in different ways. From a palaeographical point of view, the handwriting appears to belong to the Middle Kingdom rather than to the 18th dynasty.

2 - Documents on stone: two have been dated into the reign of Thutmose III:

— The Buto Stele

the offerings established by the king for the cult of this goddess (Fig. 28).

The list of feasts giving rise to these oblations is shown in the way which is usual on such monuments, i.e. in the civil calendar and in chronological order. For each feast are enumerated the items to be offered, particularly abundant on New Year's Day. There are five feasts of Wedjat, four of which fall into the winter season.

---

[12] The stele was found by the OEA and University of Tanta expedition; see J. Leclant & G. Clerc, *Orientalia* 58, p. 346. It was published by S. Bedier, *Ein Stiftungsdekret Thutmosis' III aus Buto* in M. Minas & J. Seidler, Aspekte Spätägyptischer Kultur, pp. 35-50. See also A. Spalinger, *JARCE* 33, 1996, pp. 69-76.

[13] On the sitting lion-headed Wedjat, see J.Vandier, *Ouadjet et l'Horus léontocéphale de Bouto*, excerpt from Monuments et mémoires de l'Académie des Inscriptions et Belles Lettres, Vol. 55, pp. 7-75. (For the mention of time, see pp. 45 and 52, showing a squatting spirit holding palm branches. In one case, these branches each rest on a frog, in the other, the sign *ḥb* is suspended from the branches); C. Coche, *RdE* 22, pp. 51-62. In *JNES* 8, pp. 121-123, B. Bothmer shows that the bronze statues of Wedjat sitting had been used as coffins for ichneumons.

---

[10] Published by Borchardt, *ZÄS* 37, 1899, p. 99 ff., as well as U. Luft, *Die chronologische Fixierung*, pp. 54-58, with bibliographical overview and Photo on Plate 7.

[11] See footnote 1, chapter III. The Concept.

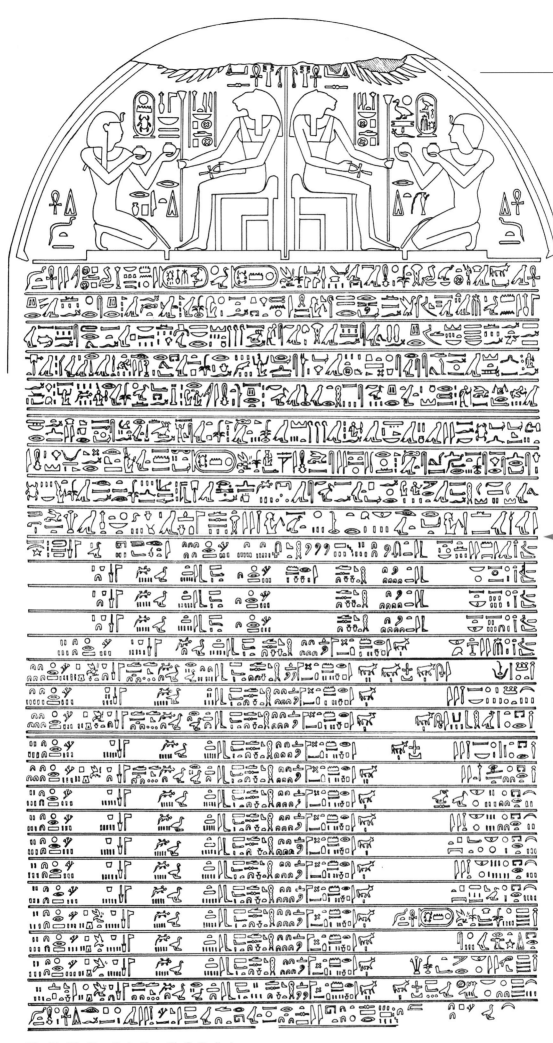

Fig. 28 - The Buto Stele (from Shafia Bedier)

Line 1	Long live **Horus**: "Mighty Bull Appeared in Thebes". **Two Ladies**: "As kingly as The One of Rah in Heaven". **Golden Horus**: "Holy in His Appearances, Mighty in Valor" **King of Upper and Lower Egypt:** "Long lasting is the Becoming of Rah" **Son of the Sun**: "Born of Thôt (= Thut-mosis), Perfect in all forms". The Lord of the Thrones of both countries, beloved by Amon Rah and Wedjat, the Mistress of Pe and Dep, may he live eternally,
Line 2	The accomplished God, child of Horus of the Horizon, who has made him to rule the lands and to rule from his father's throne, over everything under the sun on her course. The South lies in his fist, the North is subject to his will, as are both banks of the river to his glory.
Line 3	All land, all foreign countries lie subjected on his sandals, they come to him with lowered heads, bowing to his flash. All foreign rulers across the entire Earth agree: "He is our master". They have come to him out of the fear he evokes in them.
Line 4	There is no land he has not walked on to extend the frontiers of Egypt by the might of his victories. Neither millions nor hundreds of thousands can break his valour. He is a bold king who in battle creates great massacre among the Asian allies.
Line 5	He has subjected all the chiefs of the country Retenou to pay tribute and has subjected them to the annual tax, same as the people of his own House. Alone, he is more powerful than an army of many millions.
Line 6	He is such a mighty warrior that no one can equal him, not in his country, nor in his army or among the other rulers, not in the south and not in the north. He is a king who merits to enhance his valor and glory. Egypt is stronger since his reign: it fears no other country,
Line 7	nor must it worry about the South or fear the North; it knows that its protection by the King of Upper and Lower Egypt is as strong as if it came from Min. "Longlasting is the Becoming of Rah", the archer of Montou, who sets his frontier outside the limits of Egypt on foreign soil,
Line 8	the countries of Min and Kush are his subjects, offer him their production of gold in abundance, ivory and ebony without end. There is no king who has accomplished what he has, among all the kings who have lived so far.
Line 9	…my majesty commanded that the feasts of the seasonal ritual be celebrated in honour of my mother Wedjat, by divine offerings of bread, beer, beef, poultry and all good things, in great profusion and more than before.
Line 10	daily offering: (follow details concerning offerings of bread and beer, detailing the quantity of grain required for their preparation, to which are added): vegetables in bales: 50, milk: 3 jars, poultry: 1, pots of incense per month: 3.
Line 11	offerings for the *Psdntyw* feast (first day of the lunar cycle: invisibility): bread: 150, measures of beer: 10, jars of wine: 1, bales of vegetables: 10.
Line 12	offerings for the feast of **Snout** (Feast of the 6th day, 1st crescent): same offerings without wine.
Line 13	offerings for the Feast of the **15th day** (full moon): same offerings without wine.
Line 14	offerings for the Feast of the **First Evening Meal** (last day of the year, 30th day of the 4th month *šmw*. The 5 epagomenoi are not considered): bull: 1, jars of wine: 2, bread: 150, beer: 10 jars, cakes: 5, poultry: 10, incense: 5, vegetables: 25 bales.
Line 15	first month of the flood, day 1: **New Year's Feast** (abundant offerings including 4 bulls).
Line 16	3rd month of the flood, day 3, **Feast of Wedjat** (detailed offerings)
Line 17	1st month of winter, day 1, **Feast of *Nhb-k3w*** (detailed offerings)
Line 18	1st month of winter, day 2, **Feast of Wedjat** (detailed offerings)
Line 19	1st month of winter, day 20, **Feast of Wedjat's** navigation (detailed offerings)
Line 20	2nd month of winter, day 25, **Feast of Gembaous**, (detailed offerings)
Line 21	2nd month of winter, day 26, **Feast of Wedjat** (detailed offerings)
Line 22	3rd month of winter, day 1, **Feast of the Lifting of Heaven**, (detailed offerings)
Line 23	3rd month of winter, day 9, **Feast of Wedjat**, (detailed offerings)
Line 24	4th month of winter, day 1, **Feast of *ᶜq-pt*,** (detailed offerings)
Line 25	1st month of summer, day 4, **Feast of the coronation of the King of Upper and Lower Egypt**, *Mn-Hpr-Rᶜ* (Thutmose III) living forever, (detailed offerings)
Line 26	(Feast of) **Exit of Sirius**, according to his days of crossing (detailed offerings)
Line 27	1st month of summer, last day, **Feast of the *Mrt*** of the South and the North (detailed offerings)
Line 28	3rd month of summer, day 20, **Feast of the Souls of Nekhen**, (detailed offerings)

This important stele contains one of the rare mentions of the rise of Sirius with a dating in the mobile year, as can be seen in line 26: **exit of Sirius according to his days of crossing**[14].

As the following feast falls into the same month, the rise of Sirius is consequently placed in the first month of *šmw*. According to the setting, one may think that the first of these days of crossing might be day 4, the very day of the royal investiture. This would perhaps mean that the king had chosen this astronomical event of the annual reappearance of Sirius for his coronation.

---

[14]The word 𓂝𓃀𓇳 has been read as *sww*, days. It is preferable, however, to read it as *sbw*, meant as a substantival active participle "his (= Sothis') days of crossing". The crossing is, of course, the one which the date of rise follows through the mobile year, at the rate of one day every four years, moving the feast of the rise of Sirius along with it.

— The Stone of Elephantine

This engraved block (Fig. 29) has its origin most probably in the temple of Khnoum which Thutmose III had built on the island near the cataracts. It mentions a Sothis rise on the 28th day of the 3rd month of *šmw*[15].

It must be emphasised that this calendar shows an anomaly in comparison to the other documents of the same type. Habitually, the feast of the rise of Sothis inserted in the list of offerings is not given precise to the day (the date being obsolete 4 years later), but a space is simply left open and only the month is mentioned[16]. As this Elephantine

---

[15] One perceives immediately that Thutmose III could not possibly have known a reappearance in the first month of *šmw* (Buto Stele), and in the 3rd month of that same season (Elephantine Stone), since the difference represents 456 years.

[16] See A. Spalinger, *Three studies*, pp. 16-17.

Fig. 29 - The calendar of Elephantine Louvre D68 E3910 Photography: M. & P. Chuzeville

stone comes from the temple of Khnoum, deity of
the cataract and the flood, it may perhaps
commemorate the date of an earlier rise of Sirius,
occurring long before, which may have inaugurated
a salutary flood famous in people's memory, like the
one mentioned, for example, on the Stele of Famine.

— The Calendar of Medinet-Habou

On the outside of the southern wall of the
temple details are shown of the offerings instituted
by Ramses III[17]. The feast of the rise is given in the
first month of the Flood *3ḥt*[18] (Fig. 30).

In conclusion:

The establishment of chronology is far from
definite, even in its outline. If, for the last sothic
period (from 1321 B.C. to 139 A.D.), the dates
confirm one another, everything becomes topsy-
turvy in the preceding ones. A number of
impossibilities point to the fact that certain
documents must have been interpreted erroneously.
If the date on the great Buto Stele is accepted, the
ruler named in the Ebers papyrus cannot possibly be
Amenhotep I, who reigned before Thutmose III,
because the sothic date in the manuscript would
place him 260 years after. Yet, the entire current
chronology concerning the 18th dynasty is based on
this Ebers papyrus. If the Buto Stele is taken into
account, the king mentioned in the papyrus would
have reigned long before, and an entire sothic period
would have to be inserted between the Middle and
the New Kingdom. It would indeed appear highly
unlikely that the end of the 12th dynasty, the 13th –
17th dynasties, the period of the Hyksos and the
beginnings of the 18th dynasty up to the time of
Thutmose III would fit into the less than 200 years
following the Kahun letter.

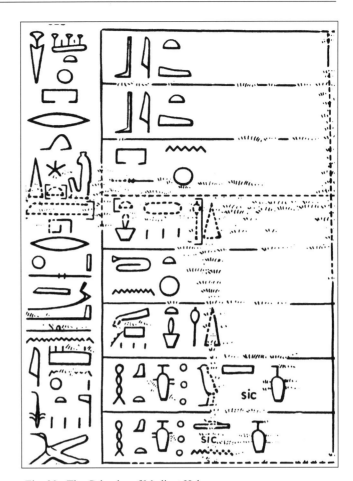

Fig. 30 - The Calendar of Medinet Habou

---

[17] *Medinet Habou*, volume III, Plates 151-152.

[18] As A. Spalinger recalls (*Three studies*, p. 16), it was R.A. Parker
(*Calendars*, p. 40) who had noted that only the month was
indicated. In absence of data, one may restore *r* (in preference of
m), this being the formula generally utilized. See A. Spalinger,
Three studies, Plates II & III, where two blocks from Karnak
(Open Air Museum) give sothic dates: one from the time of
Amenhotep I gives a rise during the first month of *prt*, a second
block indicating a rise in the fourth month of the same season.
Both carry the formula "according to his day" with *r*. The same
applies for the Buto Stele (Fig. 28).

5. The latitude of reference for the heliacal rise of Sirius

Dates of heliacal rises vary with latitude. In Egypt, stretched along the Nile flowing North down its long valley, the difference between North and South is big enough to reach several days. The annual appearance of Sirius is first observed in the South and then wanders North at the rate of approximately 1 day per degree of latitude[1], which implies a lapse of time reaching 7 days.

As this reappearance announces the New Year, according to the ancient writings, it is hard to conceive how the beginning of the year could be based on a variable footing from one part of Egypt to another. As the difference exceeds 4 days, it would perturb the counting of years as well as the sothic cycle. One may therefore argue with some logical justification, as most authors do ever since Letronne[2], **that a latitude of reference must have been chosen at the very institution of the calendar, and that it must above all else have been steadfastly maintained.**

As the star appears earlier in the country's South, some authors[3] propose Elephantine as the site of reference, particularly in view of the fact that a temple of Satet (assimilated with Sothis) was built there by Thutmose III. It is practically certain that an observatory did indeed exist in Elephantine.

Other writers prefer to think that the point of reference must have been situated in the North of Egypt, e.g. at Heliopolis, which was a well-known centre of astronomy over long periods of time. According to Strabo[4]:

"...at Heliopolis, they showed the priests' quarters as well as the schools of Plato and Eudoxus. Eudoxus had indeed come to this place with Plato, where they had lived for 13 years in the company of the priests, according to certain authors. These priests, who had very deep knowledge of celestial phenomena, were very secretive and little inclined to share their knowledge, and it was only with time and solicitude that Plato and Eudoxus obtained access to the principles of their doctrine. But these barbarians kept secret the major part of it. Nevertheless, these men gave us knowledge of the fractions of day and night which come in addition to the 365 days to complete the entire cycle of the year."

For others again, Thebes with its astronomer priests of great renown must be the site of reference. Strabo[5] further reports:

"It is said that the priests in Thebes are mostly astronomers and scholars: to the priests we owe the habit of calculating the days, not according to the moon but to the sun, and to add each year five days to the 12 months of 30 days each. And in order to make the entire year perfect, as a fraction of a day comes in excess, they form a period of time composed of an entire number of days or years so that these fractions of days, once cumulated, form an entire day. They attribute their entire science in this matter to Hermes."

Everything, however, leads to the belief that the calendar was existent in the most ancient times already, and a certain number of elements are submitted here to enhance the site of Buto as the latitude of reference for the heliacal rise.

1 - The latitude corresponding to the antique dates of heliacal rises

---

[1] For the direct observation of the rise of Sirius by Borchardt, and for calculations of the hours of re-appearance depending on degrees of latitude and day, see: L. Borchardt & O. Neugebauer, Beobachtung des Frühaufgangs des Sirius in Ägypten, *OLZ* 29, 1926, col. 309-316 and *OLZ* 30, 1927, col. 441-448. For explanation and determination of the days of reappearance according to latitude for antique times, which may be deduced from the calculations of O. Neugebauer, see R. Weill, *Chronologie*, p. 189-197.

[2] J.A. Letronne, *Nouvelles recherches sur le calendrier des Anciens Egyptiens*, p. 18.

[3] R. Krauss, *Sothis und Monddaten*, and R.A. Wells, *SAK* 12, pp. 255-302.

[4] J. Yoyotte, P. Charvet, S. Gompertz, Strabon, *Le voyage en Egypte*, XVII, 1, 29.

[5] Strabo, ibid XVII, 1, 46.

One very important point must be taken into consideration: as the Sirius and the Julian years have exactly the same duration, it follows in all logic, as Biot[6] pointed out, **that the date of the heliacal rise is practically fixed for one and the same latitude in the Julian calendar**, irrespective of the period, and certainly at least during the entire length of Egyptian history[7].

It must therefore be of interest to determine the latitude to which the Julian dates of the rises mentioned in antiquity correspond. **We may reasonably conclude that that must be the latitude of reference, especially if one such rise inaugurated the great cycle of 1460 years**. As Censorinus indicates the beginning of the sothic period of 139 AD, he speaks of the rise of Sirius "for Egypt", which must mean that that date was indeed valid for the entire country. It corresponds to the Julian July 20th (or more precisely: the night of the Julian 19th to 20th of July).

This same date of July 19th to 20th is confirmed by a number of antique authors cited by Letronne[8]. Like Biot, he admits that the star is only visible if the sun still stands 11° or 12° below the horizon[9]. Gathering together the ancient sources, Letronne further concludes that the date is valid for the latitude of Memphis or Heliopolis. Since Borchardt[10] personally observed the rise of Sirius, we know that that very brilliant star is visible even if the sun is only 9° 4' below the horizon. And the tables compiled by Neugebauer and commented on by Weill[11] connect the date with the latitude of Alexandria.

2 - An antique town on the latitude of Alexandria

The ancient and mythical town of Buto, like Alexandria, is sited slightly above latitude 31° North. It is often connected with the observation of the sky during the New Year rites and by the rituals recalling the foundation of the temples where its name appears. The ceremonies begin during the night, and the precise location of the stakes over which the rope is tended, is decided by the king and the goddess Sefekht-Aboui, depending on the sighting of the stars[12] through the merkhet[13].

The town is associated more precisely with New

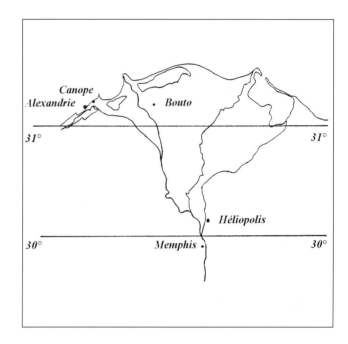

Fig. 31 - Lower Egypt

---

6 J.B. Biot, *Traité élémentaire d'astronomie physique IV*, p. 640.

7 We have seen (see note 4, p. 28) that according to his calculations, the difference would only reach one day in 5000 years.

8 See J.A. Letronne, *Nouvelles recherches*, pp. 28-36 with references; also E. Meyer, *Chronologie Egyptienne*, transl. A. Moret, pp.26-28.

9 For the arc of vision see p. 26, chapt. II. Sirius and the sothic year.

10 L. Borchardt could observe Sirius appear on (Gregorian) Aug. 3, 1925, (i.e. Julian July 21), at Ghizah (30° N latitude), while the sun stood 9°4' below the horizon (see footnote 1, p. 46 for ref.).

11 R. Weill, *Chronologie Egyptienne*, pp. 190-196 and *Compléments* pp. 27-37.

12 Sefekht-Aboui (= the one with 7 prongs) is a name for Seshat, alluding to the instrument she wears on her head (see cover page 4). Discourse: "...I have seized a piquet, I have taken the club, directing our two faces according to the course of the stars, letting our glance enter the constellation of the Big Dipper (*Msht*). He who kills the time (*Sq-ʿhʿ* - Thôt) is beside his merkhet", according to P. Montet, *Kemi*, 17, p. 78, and for Buto see P. Barguet, *RdE* 9, p. 2.

13 For the merkhet, see L. Borchardt, *ZÄS* 37, pp. 10-17; R.W. Sloley, *JEA* 17, p. 170 and Plate 16; G. Goyon, *Le secret des bâtisseurs des grandes pyramides*, pp. 89-91.

Year's Day, due to the ceremonies confirming the royal power. These took place at Buto in very early days[14]. The "consolidation of inheritance"[15] (*smn iw't*) are rites of New Year's Day, of the five epagomenoi and of the 9th day of the first month of *3ḫt*[16]. We also know that at the time of their coronation, the kings usually went on a pilgrimage to the place.

At the time of the first dynasties, the sign of the year already appears on ivory labels[17], which indicates the existence of a calendar, and records are kept since the very beginning of historical times[18]. If the gliding calendar dates from this period, Buto could well be the site of reference for the annual rise of Sirius.

3 - Possible antiquity of the institution of the double calendar

Many testimonials attribute a long practice of astronomy[19] to Egypt. The observation of rising stars which determined the hours of the night, is documented in the Old Kingdom already as being practiced on the temple terraces[20].

On the ivory plate of King Djer[21] of the 1st

Fig. 32 - Djer's tablet (from Petrie)

dynasty, Altenmüller[22] noticed the first proof of the relation between the rise of Sirius, depicted as a cow as in Dendera, and the onset of the flood. On this plate, too, Petrie[23] found the site of Buto mentioned (Fig. 32).

Although the interpretation has been contested[24], the image of the cow (Sekhathor or Sothis) with the sign of Shu between her horns, strongly evokes the reading "opening of the year", especially above the sign *3ḫt*. The sign of the feather between the horns recalls that Thôt, under the aspect of the god Shu, went to Nubia[25] in search of the Distant One[26] for the return of the flood[27]. The heavenly cow, feeder and protector of Pharaoh and Egypt, impersonates at the

[14] A. Gutgub, *Kemi* 16, note 11 pp. 46-47 and *Kemi*, 17, p. 51.

[15] J.C. Goyon, *Confirmation du pouvoir royal*, p. 72. In the Edfu ritual, the date is the 1st day of the 1st month of *prt*: J.C. Goyon, *Confirmation*, p. 45. On the dates of the 1st day of *3ḫt* and of the 1st day of *prt*, both treated as New Year, see the references in A. Spalinger, *Three Studies*, p. 48 note 76, and *SAK* 17, 289-294.

[16] The day called in Esna "The New Year of the Ancestors": S. Sauneron, *Les fêtes religieuses d'Esna* V, p. 11.

[17] W. Petrie, *The Royal Tomb of the First Dynasty* I, Plate XV, 16.

[18] E. Hornung, *L'esprit du temps des Pharaons*, French transl., pp. 156-160.

[19] Diodor of Sicily (Diodorus Siculus), I, 71: *"There is perhaps no other country where order and movement of the stars are observed with such exactitude as in Egypt, since an incredible number of years, they keep registers where their observations are written down". Diodore does not elaborate on that number of years which he qualifies as "incredible".*

[20] P. Posener-Kriéger, *Les archives du temple funéraire de Neferirkare Kakaï*, Plates 3, 5, 11, 12 and 87A, Commentaire tome I, pp. 31-34.

[21] W. Petrie, *Royal Tombs* II, p. 22 and Plate 5 (1).

[22] H. Altenmüller, *Die Apotropaïa und die Götter Mittelägyptens*, p. 127, sees in this monument the proof that since the most ancient times, Sothis was considered as the mother of Rah.

[23] W. Petrie, *Royal Tombs* II, p. 22.

[24] G. Godron, *BIFAO* 57, p. 147; A. Spalinger, *Three Studies*, p. 46; M. Clagett, *Ancient Egyptian Science* II, pp. 10-11.

[25] The flood comes from the South, and Sirius is a Southern star.

[26] C. Desroches Noblecourt, *Le petit temple d'Abou-Simbel*, pp. 115-116.

[27] An inundation related to the sun in the summer solstice.

same time Hathor, Sothis, Isis, Sekhmet and Wedjat[28]. In addition, at Dendera[29], Sekhathor, too, is identified with Hathor. The feather of Shu between the horns of the cow on the plate of Djer is often seen as an element of the headdressing of Sothis in astronomical compositions, and is, incidentally, often shown with the disk of the sun above it (Fig. 33).

---

[28] Concerning the syncretism of these goddesses, see J. Yoyotte, *BSFE* 87-88, pp. 52-59. See above all p. 58 for the rite of appeasing Sekhmet and the role of the ouadj of Sekhmet

[29] Dendera I, 130 (S. Cauville, *Denderah* I, pp. 192-193). For the identification of Hathor with Sekhmet, Bastet, Wedjat and Sothis, see *Dendera* I, 5 (S. Cauville, *Denderah* I, pp. 16-19); in that last passage, Wedjat is called "the One who protects the child in its nest"; the night of the "child in its nest" is precisely the name of the 5th epagomene, date or the reappearance of Sirius in the fixed year.

It is not senseless to think that it is Sothis who faces the cartouche of King Djer, a point which should be retained. Only the discovery of further data could contest its first interpretation, or accept it as an element in favour of the great antiquity of the installation of the double calendar. The same goes for the possibility to consider Buto as the site of reference of the rise of Sothis, since the town fulfils both the geographical and historical conditions of correct latitude and of high antiquity. It is definitely of interest to know for certain the site of reference; on the other hand, it must be said that its definition is not essential for sothiac chronology, as long as the beginning of each sothic period is determined "for Egypt".

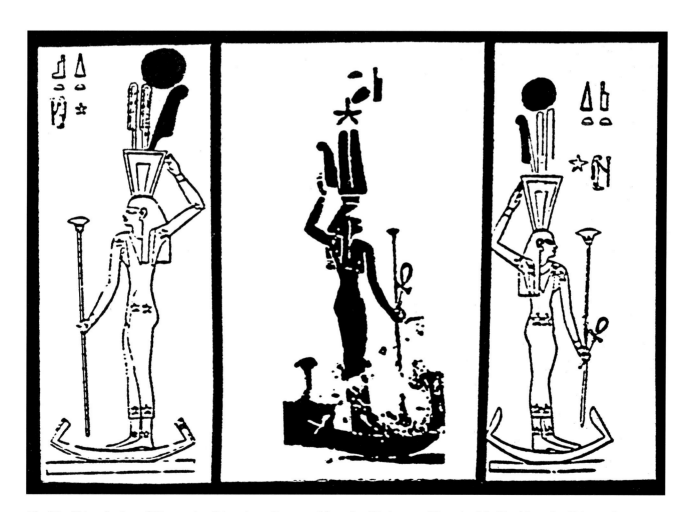

Fig. 33 - Sirius: feather of Shou, solar disk and ouadj sceptre (a) tomb of Pedamon - (b) tomb of Seti I - (c) tomb of Montemhet (from Neugebauer & Parker)

II. The decans

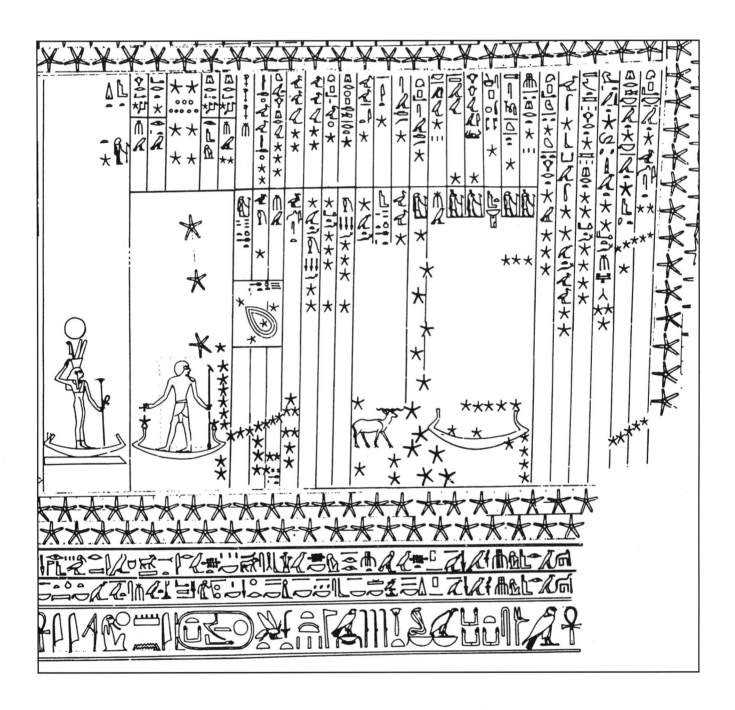

Fig. 34 - The decans - Ceiling of the Tomb of Senmut

1 - Zodiac and decans

The considerable difference between the three "decans" of each of the twelve constellations of the zodiac on the one hand, and the Egyptian decans on the other must be clearly pointed out both from the historical and from the functional point of view.

The groupings known as the zodiac only appear in the Egyptian civilisation towards its end, and they are undoubtedly of foreign inspiration[1]. They are of very markedly unequal duration, which limits their astronomical interest, and to divide the year on their basis would lack precision.

The Egyptian decan, on the contrary,

corresponds to a very precise function, and the way in which it was originally defined still has repercussions to this very day. In addition, there is a strong presumption that it constitutes the very backbone of the calendaric construction.

It is difficult to ascertain exactly when the decans first appear. They are called *ᶜnḫw*, "the living", which is a euphemism opposed to the circumpolar stars, *iḫmw-sk*, "those who do not know destruction". Contrary to the perennially visible constellations near the North Pole, the decan, like a living being, is born, lives, dies and vanishes into the Douat during its period of invisibility. There are 36 decans, and they separate the year very precisely into 36 periods of 10 days, hence their name of "decans"[2].

---

[1] On evolution of the zodiacal signs, see C. Desroches Noblecourt, *Archaeologia* 292, pp. 21-45.

[2] Making up the year of 360 days; see M. Clagett, *Ancient Egyptian Science* II, p. 5.

Fig. 35 - Tomb of Senmut, the decans, detail (Photo K. Locher)

2 - The names of the decans

Each decan has a name[3] which is mentioned in numerous astronomical texts found in temples, tombs, on coffins and water clocks. Their name is often accompanied by a group of stars and sometimes even by drawings of constellations; one can discern a boat, for instance, centred by the decan *ḥry-ib-wꜣ3*, or a ewe (decan *srt*, see Fig. 34).

The decanal cycle, heralded by the appearance of Sirius[4], begins with the group *ḥnmt* or *tp-ꜥ-ḥnmt*, and ends with the decans of the Orion group.

Each decan has its own deities attached. On the ceiling of the tomb of Seti I[5] in the Valley of the Kings, these deities can be found painted in gold. They advance from East to West, grouped together by two or three, against a background of night blue (Fig. 36, 37).

---

[3] For the names of the decans, see H. Brugsch, *Thesaurus*, pp. 18-23; E.A.W. Budge, *The Gods of the Egyptians*, vol. II, pp. 304-308; O. Neugebauer & R.A. Parker, *EAT* I, pp. 2-3, 24-26 and Plates 26-29 and *EAT* III, pp. 105-174.

[4] Sirius is qualified in Dendera as the Sovereign of the Decans; H. Brugsch, *Thesaurus*, p. 107. The papyrus Carlsberg I (II, 36-37) states that according to the book "*Šꜣ idnw*" : "...all these stars begin on the 1st *ꜣḫt* when Sirius appears". The same sentence can be found on the cenotaph of Seti I (see *EAT* I, p. 54). Sirius itself often appears as a decan. But on the other hand, it is also specified in Carlsberg I (II, 41) that according to the book "*Bnn*" "...Sirius has 18 decans after her and 18 decans before her" (*EAT* I p. 55).

[5] See O. Neugebauer & R.A. Parker, *EAT* III, Plate 3 (the reference being Seti I C); E. Hornung, *The Tomb of Pharao Seti I*, pp. 240-241.

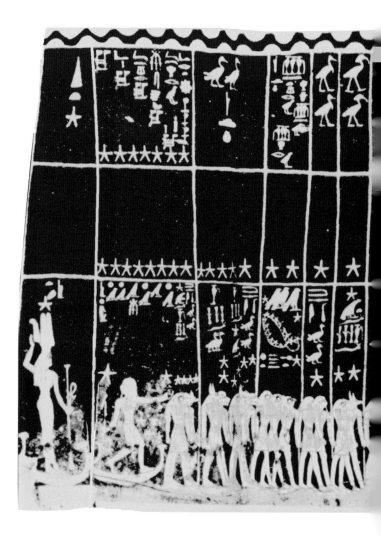

Fig. 37 - The names of the decans and their divinities.
Tomb of Seti I.

Fig. 36 - Tomb of Seti I. Valley of the Kings.

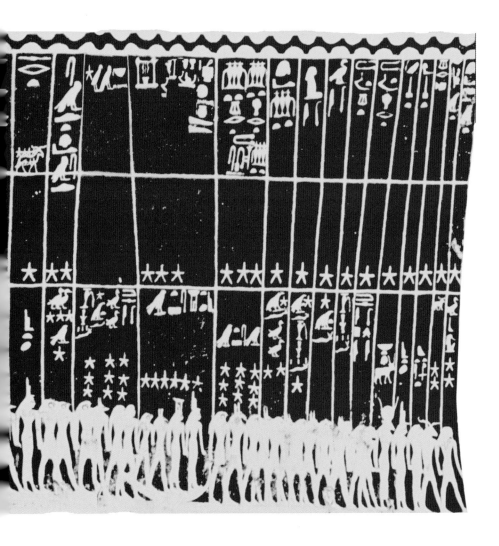

3 - Identification of the decans

The problem with identification of the stars in the Egyptian decans is first to know where exactly was positioned what is called "the decanal belt", i.e. the band of the celestial sphere which contained the decans. Opinions differ on the subject[6]. One recent publication[7] offering an identification of the constellations of the Northern sky and the belt of the Egyptian decans (Fig. 38), suggests that *ṯms-n-ḫntt* ("Red of the bow") should be identified[8] with Antares, situated, according to that text, at the head of the boat which contains *ḥry-ib-wi3*.

4 - Definition and function of a decan

A decan is a star which indicates one and the same hour during 10 days, either by its heliacal rise[9], or by its culmination[10]. Due to the progress of the Earth on its orbit around the sun, any star which has reappeared in the East[11] after its period of invisibility, will be seen progressively earlier during the night (Fig. 21, 44). First seen in the 12th hour at the very end of the night, the decanal star will 10 days later already be visible at the 11th hour, another 10 days later at the 10th hour for the following decade, etc... Irrespective of whether the hours are determined by the heliacal rise or the culmination of the star, one and the same decan will work during:

10 days from the end of the 12th hour to the beginning of the 12th hour marking the 12th hour.

10 days from the beginning of the 12th hour to the beginning of the 11th hour, marking the 11th hour.

10 days from the beginning of the 11th hour to the beginning of the 10th hour, marking the 10th hour.

10 days from the beginning of the 10th hour to the beginning of the 9th hour, marking the 9th hour.

10 days from the beginning of the 9th hour to the beginning of the 8th hour, marking the 8th hour.

10 days from the beginning of the 8th hour to the beginning of the 7th hour, marking the 7th hour.

10 days from the beginning of the 7th hour to the beginning of the 6th hour, marking the 6th hour.

10 days from the beginning of the 6th hour to the beginning of the 5th hour, marking the 5th hour.

10 days from the beginning of the 5th hour to the beginning of the 4th hour, marking the 4th hour.

10 days from the beginning of the 4th hour to the beginning of the 3rd hour, marking the 3rd hour.

10 days from the beginning of the 3rd hour to the beginning of the 2nd hour, marking the   2nd hour.

10 days from the beginning of the 2nd hour to the beginning of the 1st hour, marking the   1st hour.

In total, this is a "work" of 120 days. If we suppose that it is the culmination which matters, then after 120 days, the decan has passed into the West when night comes and does not culminate any longer – it has finished its work. In practice, it seems very difficult to find a star at exactly the right place in the sky, and for each hour, fulfilling exactly all the required conditions of position and of brilliance. Which is why each decan consists of several stars which share, according to circumstances, and certainly according to the time of year, the work of heralding the hours of the night.

---

[6] For O. Neugebauer & R.A. Parker, *EAT* I, pp. 97-100, the decanal belt is situated on a parallel South of the ecliptic. For the evolution of ideas on this controversial matter see K. Locher, *New Arguments for the Celestial Location of the Decanal Belt and for the origin of the s3H-hieroglyph*, IV. Congresso internazionale di Egittologia, Atti II, Torino 1993, pp. 279-280.

[7] K. Locher, *New Arguments*, graph p. 283: we have transposed only the decanal belt and not the constellations of the northern sky.

[8] As did R. Böker, *Centaurus* 27, 1984, pp. 189-217.

[9] For the Egyptians, this is the birth of a star.

[10] The moment of its standing in the meridian.

[11] The visible heliacal rise of the star.

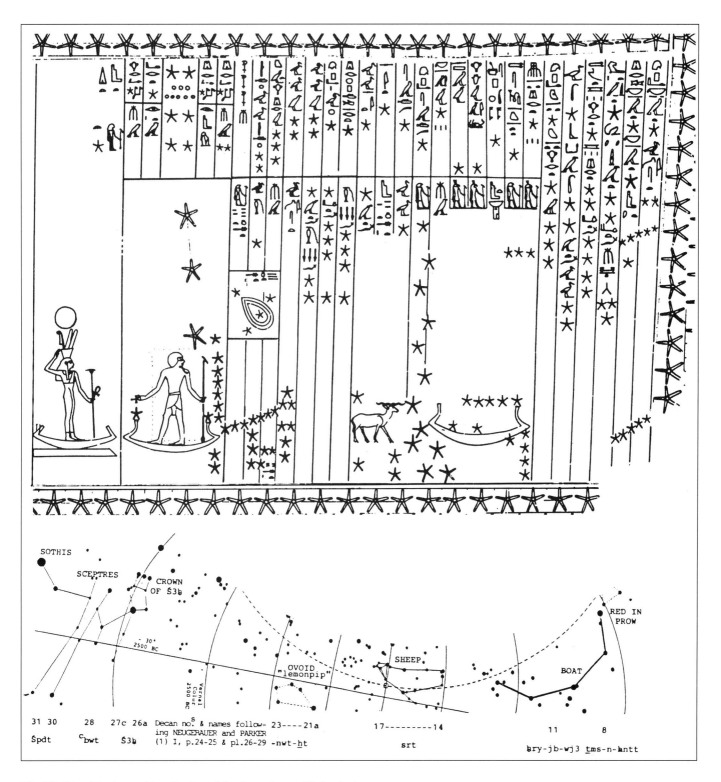

Fig. 38 - Identification and localisation of the decanal stars (K. Locher).

Comparison with the list of Senmut (the curved dotted line representing the ecliptic).

5 - The lists of decans

Coffins of the 9th, 10th, and 11th dynasty show hourly tables[12], with the name of the decan marking each of the 12 hours of the night, for the 36 decades of the year. Months are divided into three decades: *tp*, the first, *ḥry-ib*, the middle one and *pḥwy*, the last, making a decan rise diagonally from the 12th to the 1st hour, in 120 days (Fig. 39).

Sirius is also depicted on these hourly tables on the coffins, and is thus connected with a date in the mobile year; this is why these monuments have been utilised for purposes of chronology. The calculations differ, however, depending on whether the appearance of Sirius at the 12th hour on these tables is understood as the date of its heliacal rise or that of its culmination[13].

---

[12] O. Neugebauer & R.A. Parker, *EAT* I, pp. 1-22, Plates 1-23; K. Locher, *JHA* n° 23, 1992, pp. 201-207. For the astronomical study, see Ch. Leitz, *Altägyptische Sternuhren*, pp. 58-116.

---

[13] The difference is slightly over 3 centuries. In the Senmut table and later documents, it is the culmination of the star which marks the hour. It would seem more logical if that were the case for the coffins, too.

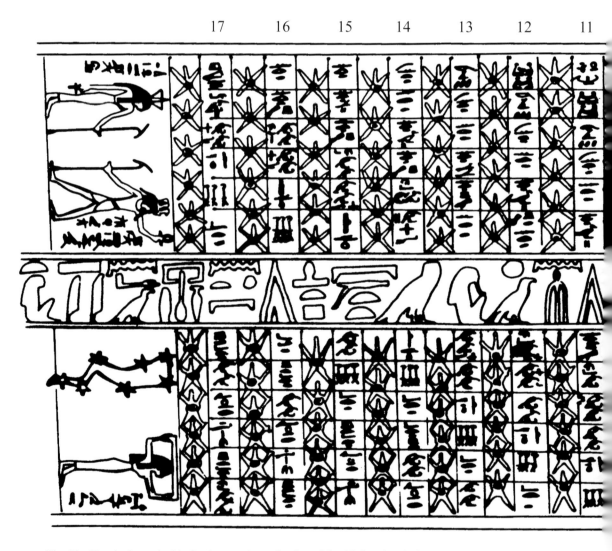

Fig. 39 - Hourly decanal table for the year (reproduction of the 17 first decades).

(O. Neugebauer &. R.A. Parker, Sarcophagus Nr. 6)

Comparing the Senmut list with these ancient tables, O. Neugebauer & R.A. Parker showed[14] that they were arranged in the same way as on the coffins, although simplified. The first columns in Senmut show the decans of the 12 night hours of the 1st decade of the year; the decans above the horizontal line are those of all the 12th night hours of the following decades (Fig. 38).

[14] *EAT* I, pp. 22-23.

←——— the decades of the year

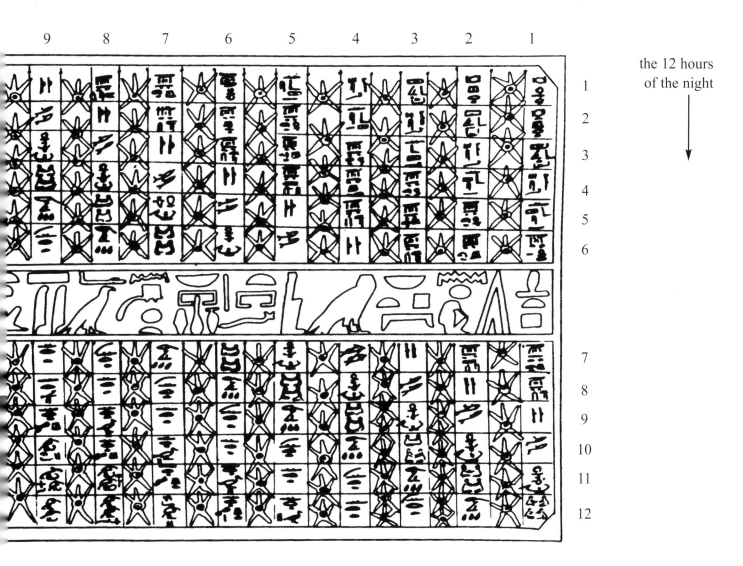

the 12 hours of the night
↓

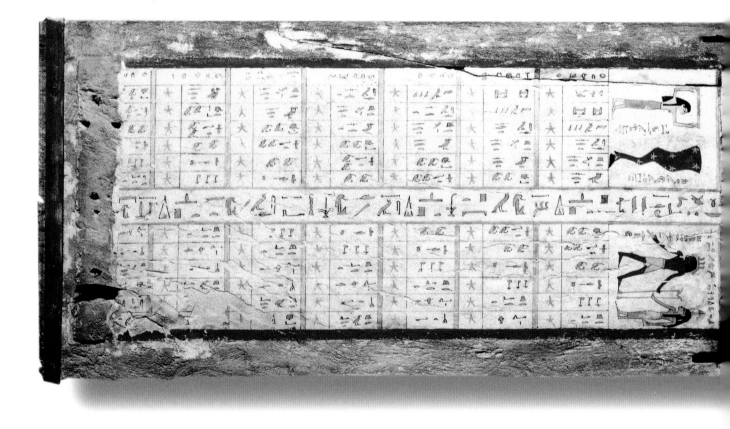

Fig.40 - Hourly decanal table, sarcophagus of Idy (Sarcophagus Nr. 4, O. Neugebauer &. R.A. Parker, Photo University of Tübingen)

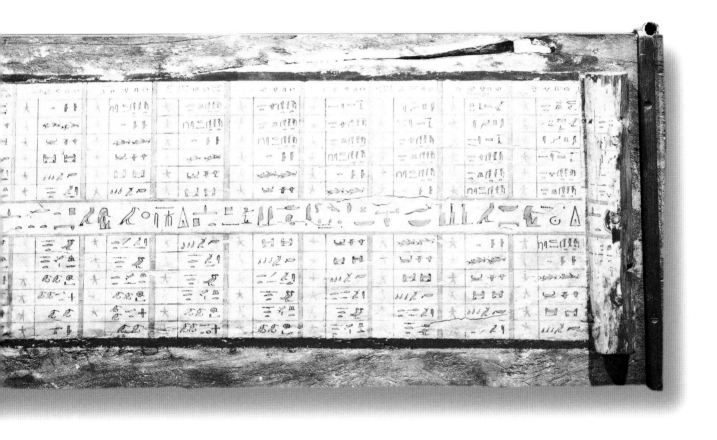

Some monuments, like a naos of which the Louvre owns a fragment (Fig. 41), show the decans under various different aspects[15] and relate them to the god Sopedu and the locality of *Ḥwt-nbs*[16] (in the neighbourhood of Saft El-Hennah), situated in the 20th nome of Lower Egypt.

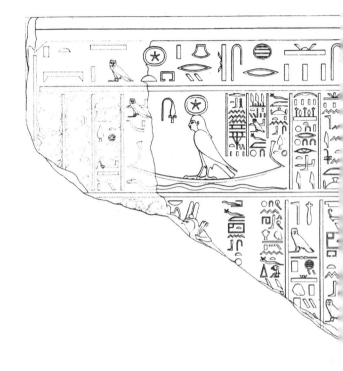

---

[15] The lower part of this naos is in the graeco-roman Museum in Alexandria; a further part of this monument was recently found by the IEASM mission under F. Goddio, who permitted its reproduction of figure 42. This discovery will soon be published separately. References: *Description de l'Egypte*, Antiquity, V, Plate 48, Figures 5-6; P. Pierret, *Recueil d'inscriptions inédites du Musée du Louvre II*, p. 73; H. Brugsch, *Thesaurus*, pp. 180-182; J.J. Clère *JNES* 9, 1950, 143-152; L Habachi et B.Habachi, *JNES* 11, 1952, p.251-263; J. Yoyotte, *JNES* 13, 1954, pp. 79-82; Ch. Leitz, *Altägyptische Sternuhren*, pp. 3-57.

[16] In the capital of the same nome.

Fig. 41 - The Louvre Calendar or naos of the decades. (from Description de l'Egypte)

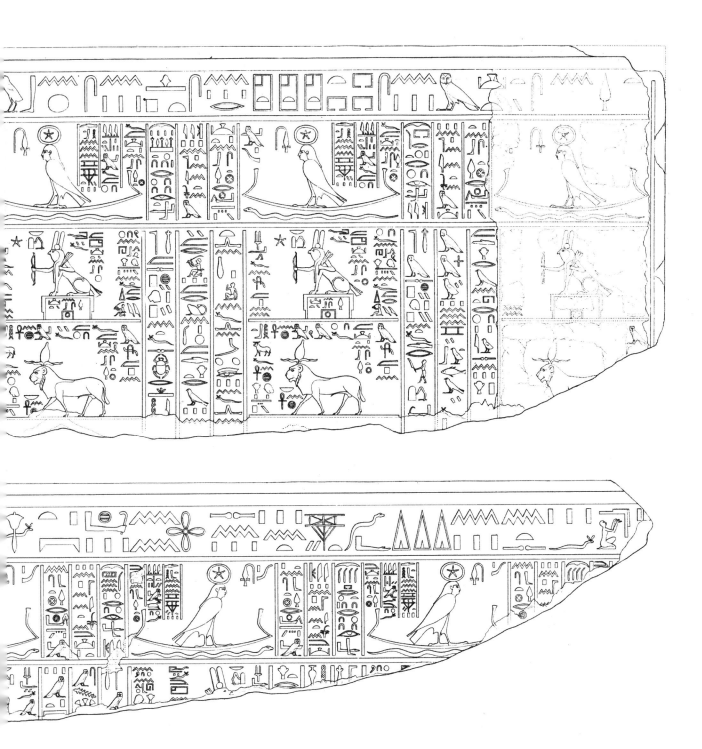

One of the forms of the decan is that of a bird with a human head covered by a star contained in a circle ⊗ , representing the Douat, the inferior hemisphere (fig. 42).

Fig. 42 - One aspect of the decans on a recently discovered fragment of the naos of the decades (IEASM, Photo Ch. Gerigk, UAD)

6 - Decans and epagomenoi: the decanal structure of the year

The 36 decades add up to a year of 360 days. The simple observation that the 5 additional days are kept apart and defined as "in addition to the year", demonstrates that the structure of the years is above all decanal (Fig. 43).

The year does indeed count 12 months following the cycles of the moon. But these months are invariably composed of 30 days, i.e. 3 decades, and this division into decades seems to be more important than the phases of the moon[17].

It is even more interesting to observe that in the ceiling of Senmut's tomb (Fig. 10), the circles representing the months are divided into 24 portions according to the number of hours, instead of 30 for the number of lunar days. This seems to indicate that

the month is much more strongly characterised by the length of the hours, linked to the decans, rather than the duration of the lunar cycle. This notion of the relationship between the months and the hours can also be found in documents which indicate the respective length of the day and the night for each month[18], but also, of course, on the water clocks whose internal calibration varies according to the month. (see p.66 unequal hours)

The year, built around the definition of the decanal stars, and whose length is measured between two heliacal appearances of Sirius, thus appears to be essentially stellar and only very incidentally lunar.

The 5 epagomenoi of the fixed and the mobile year are counted at the end of the year and outside of it. On the decanal lists of the coffins, which concern the mobile year divided into sections of 10 days, they appear after the 36 decades[19], with hourly markers proper to them. In the calendar representations, the "decans" of the epagomenoi are treated separately, apart from the decanal cycle, between the external and internal planets (Fig. 53).

---

[17] As an example, in the archives of the temple of Neferirkare-Kakaï, one can see a feast of the new moon on day 17 in a table divided into decades, instead of at the head of the list (P. Posener-Krieger, *HPBM* V, Plate V). In the temple of Illahun, on the other hand, the change of personnel is organised according to the lunar cycles: H. Borchardt, *ZÄS* 37, pp. 92-93; R. A. Parker, *Calendars*, p. 37; U. Luft, *Die chronologische Fixierung*, p. 189 ff. But although the lunar feast days are evidently very important for cultual reasons, it must be noted that the phases of the moon are related to the civil year, which seems to indicate that there never existed a separate lunar calendar.

---

[18] As, for instance, the papyrus Cairo 86637: A.M. Bakir, *Cairo Calendar*, Plates 44-45; Ch. Leitz, *Tagewählerei*, Plate 44; or the text II of Tanis, J.J. Clère, *Kemi* 10, 1949, pp. 8-9.

[19] O. Neugebauer & R.A. Parker, *EAT* I, The epagomenoi are depicted on the coffins 1, 6, 7 and 8. For an explanation of the "decanal triangle", see O. Neugebauer & R.A. Parker, *EAT* I, pp. 1-2 and 22-23 with Fig. 14, as well as *EAT* III, pp. 116-118 and 124-128.

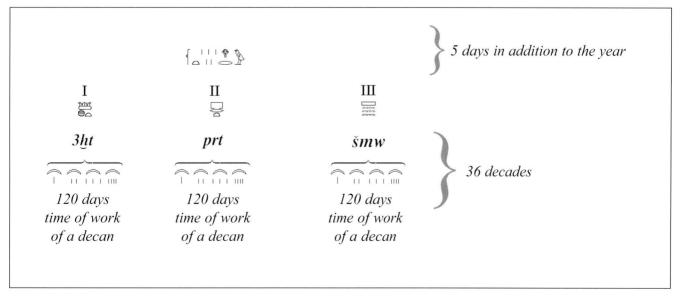

Fig. 43 - Decanal structure of the mobile year. Each of the 3 periods amounts to 120 days, i.e. the entire course of a decan.

7 - Decans, hours, cosmography and geodesy

The division of the night into 12 units has its origin, as O. Neugebauer and R.A. Parker have demonstrated, directly in the choice of 36 stars and the interval of 10 days between the appearance of each star[20]. It is this division of the day into 24 hours which we still use today[21].

One may go even further, if the relation between the Earth's rotation (around its own axis = duration of the day divided into 24 hours) and orbit (around the sun = duration of the year with the successive appearance of 36 decans) is to be taken into account. In the course of the year, a new decan culminates in the 12th hour every 10 days (see Fig. 44), while the preceding decan marks the 11th hour, and so on. But as the Earth rotates around its own axis during the night, the same decans will, in fact, define the hour's interval (Fig. 45).

There clearly emerges the intention to create a direct relationship between the hour (as a segment of the time of the earthly rotation) and the year (the time of the terrestrial orbit): during one night, a new decan culminates every 60 minutes (this is the length of the hour); but during a year, the progression of a decan's culmination is only of 40 minutes. The equivalence could be established[22] thanks to the duodecimal system, i.e. by determining the duration and the number of hours according to the number of days in the year (time of orbit revolution). Only the number of 360 days could create a simple relationship between the year (360 days), the month (12 months of 30 days), the day (360th part of the decanal year with 12 hours per day and 12 hours per night), and the hour (24th part of the time of rotation).

Taking now a look at the degrees of longitude, it becomes clear that due to the rotation of the Earth, the culminating point of a star (or the sun) will be seen successively on the different longitudes, moving along the Earth from East to West. For each additional degree of longitude westward, the culmination point comes 4 minutes later. In addition, any star will see its culmination advance (as an average) by 4 minutes per day due to the Earth's orbit. Obviously, there can be no room for happenstance: the data obtained through observation of the phenomena pertaining to the Earth's orbit have controlled the choices which have guided not only the manner of dividing the time of rotation (i.e. into hours), but also that of 360° to divide the circle[23], after the number of decans, which is itself related to the 360 days. All astronomical definitions implied by the decan are closely linked to terrestrial[24] measuring and to cosmography[25].

---

[23] Even if the terms of "degree" or of "angular velocity" have not been found or identified in the Egyptian texts, one can only acknowledge that these notions have been well understood and utilised.

[24] Longitudes are measured as 0-180° East and West, latitudes in 0-90° North or South. The degree, like the hour, is divided into 60 minutes.

[25] Which seems to accredit Greek assertions that the Egyptians had great astronomical knowledge, and had created cosmography and geodesy.

---

[20] O. Neugebauer & R.A. Parker, *EAT* I, p. 116.

[21] This is the origin of our time zones.

[22] The progress of one and the same decan through the year of 360 days is calculated as follows: 40 min. x 36 = 1440 minutes = 24 hours. The equivalence was possible on the condition that the epagomenoi were not taken into account. **This is very probably the essential reason for which they were kept apart and defined as "in addition to the year".** It is amusing to notice that if the additional progress during the 5 epagomenoi (= ½ décade) is taken into account, 20 minutes must be added, resulting in 1440 + 20 = 1460 minutes, i.e. the same number as the sothic tetraery or the years of the sothic period.

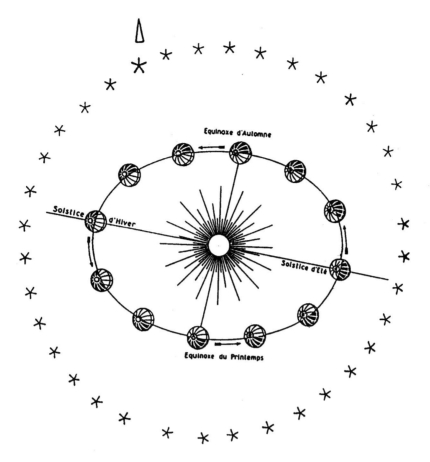

Fig. 44 - Orbit: the 36 decanal stars of the year.

Due to the Earth's annual course on its orbit a new star appears every 10 days.

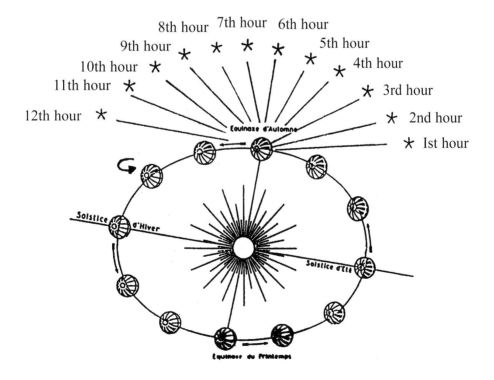

Fig. 45 - Rotation: the 12 decans working during one night due to the Earth's rotation around its own axis. Each of these stars indicates one hour of the night. On each equinox, each of these 12 nightly hours equals the 24th part of a day.

8 - Equal and unequal hours

At either equinox, days and nights have the same duration and the hour, then truly equalling the 24th part of the time of the Earth's rotation, is called the equinoxial hour. But the Earth's axis is oblique relative to the level of her orbit, which determines the seasons. The nights are thus of unequal length, short in summer and long in winter. It is probably for cultual reasons that the Egyptians divided the unequal nights into 12 equal parts, using clepsydrae (i.e. water clocks) for this purpose. The oldest one goes as far back as Amenhotep III[26] (Fig. 12 & 46).

The internal gradations of these water clocks give the length of the night hours depending on the month of the year.

The image of a clepsydra can be found in certain tombs[27] (Fig. 47); the figures along the sides are the Night Hours, and as they are disposed, they seem to follow each other. Before the central personage one can find the summer sun rising high in the sky, and behind it, lower, the winter sun with longer nights.

To measure the hours of the day, the Egyptians used shadow clocks[28] (Fig. 49).

[26] G. Daressy, BIE, series 5.9, pp. 5-16; L. Borchardt, *Zeitmessung*, pp. 6-7, Plates 1-3; R. Sloley, *JEA* 17, pp. 174-176; R.A. Parker, *Calendars*, p. 40; O. Neugebauer & R.A. Parker, *EAT* III, pp. 12-13 and Plate 2. Further B. Cotterell, F.P. Dickson, J. Kamminga, *J. Archaeol,. Sci.* 14, 1986, pp. 31-50; L. Dupuydt, *Civil Calendar and Lunar Calendar*, pp. 112-113. For the period prior to the invention of the clepsydra see R.A. Wells, *BSAK* 4, pp. 95-104 and *SAK* 20, pp. 305-326.

[27] The tombs of Taousert, Ramses III, Ramses VI, Ramses IX, Ramesseum sarcophagus; see P. Barguet, *RdE* 30, p. 53.

[28] R. Sloley, *JEA 17*, pp. 170-174; O. Neugebauer & R.A. Parker, *EAT I*, pp. 116-121; M. Isler, *JARCE 28*, 1991, pp. 155-185; S. Symons, *BSS* 98, 3, pp.30-36.

Fig. 46 - the water clock dating from Amenhotep III (Le Grand Pharaon Ramsès II et son temps, Exhibition catalogue, 1985)

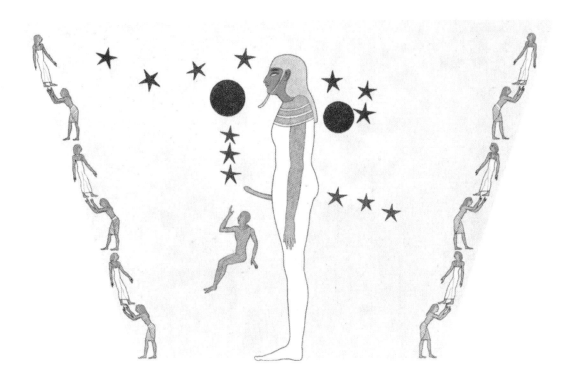

Fig. 47 - Water clock and hours of the night (Description d'Egypte).

Fig. 48 - Tomb of Ramses VI, 20th dynasty. Representation of a water clock in section 6 of the Book of Caverns.

On such a clock, the first hour of the day can only be determined when the sun rises[29] to project a shadow; hence its name *wbnwt*[30]. The object below, a portable one, is calibrated for the North of Egypt.

The Egyptians thus used both the equinoxial hours as defined by the decans, and the temporary hours of variable length depending on the month of the year. One of the sides of the cubits seems to show indications for setting clepsydrae and shadow clocks depending on the month[31].

---

[29] The sixth hour (noon) whose name "the standing one" expresses the vertical shadow, marks the passage of the 6th to the 7th hour, i.e. the end of the hour. Thus *wbnwt* marks the end of the first hour, which leads to the supposition that the beginning (and therewith the beginning of the day) took place at dawn, before sunrise. For the beginning of the day at *ḥḏ-t3* see J. von Beckerath, ZÄS 120, p.21 and R. Krauss, *BSEG* 14, pp. 54-56; A. Spalinger in *ZÄS* 119, p.155.

[30] For the name of the divinities of the hours see H. Brugsch, *Thesaurus*, p. 28 and 31, as well as E.A.W. Budge, *The Gods of the Egyptians*, Vol. II, pp. 300-302

[31] A. Schlott, *Die Ausmaße Ägyptens nach altägyptischen Texten*, p. 50, (text g).

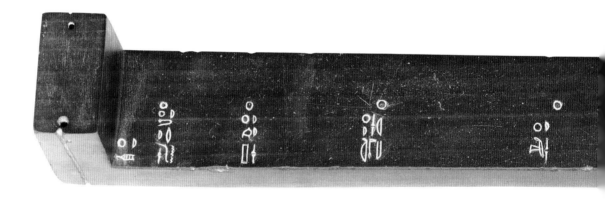

Fig. 49 - Shadow clock: from the 1st to the 6th hour of the day. Berlin Museum 19743. (Photo Jutta Tietz).

In conclusion:

The equinoxial hour has been defined according to the length of the year: a new decan culminates every 10 days, the complete course of 360° is accomplished in 360 days (1° per day): clearly, the frame of the calendar based on these divisions is decanal in nature. 12 sets of 3 decades constitute 12 months, following the cycles of the moon. Five days "outside the year" are added to complete the mobile year of 365 days. The missing $1/4$ day is taken into account at each annual rise of Sirius, but the additional day thus generated each fourth year is skipped by the gliding movement.

Fig. 50 - Dendera, ceiling of the entrance to the hypostyle (Photo K. Locher)

The Planets

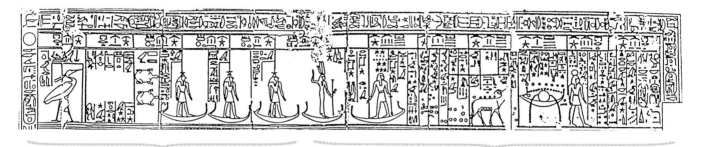

Planets and epagomene decans   Decanal cycle

Fig. 51 - Ramesseum – Upper register.

Although they were termed alike: ⟨hieroglyph⟩, *sb3*, planets and stars were clearly differentiated[1] and were grouped together in the eastern part of the upper register of representations (Fig. 51). Together with the "decans" of the epagomenoi, they are set apart, whereas the 36 decanal stars, which constitute an entity in themselves, occupy all the western part of that register.

1. Internal and external planets

The planets are disposed in two groups, internal and external planets, on either side of the "decans" of the epagomenoi (Figs. 51 and 53).

The terms 'internal' and 'external' relate to their orbits: two of the five planets visible to the human eye (Venus and Mercury) move on an orbit inside that of the Earth (i.e. closer to the sun), and three (Mars, Saturn and Jupiter) move on one outside (Fig. 52).

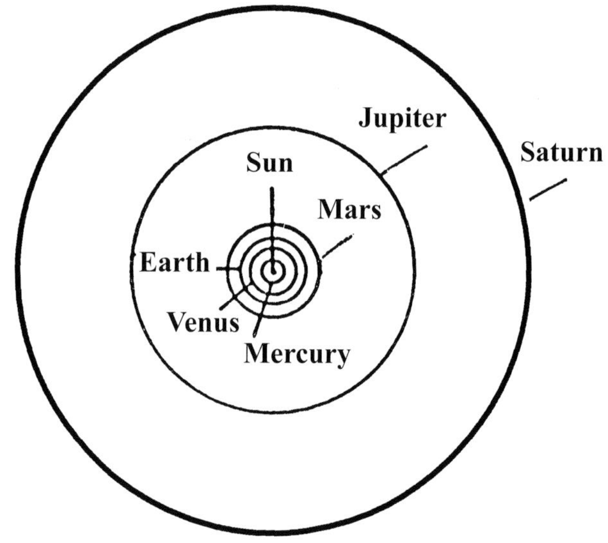

Fig. 52 - Orbits of the five planets visible to the naked eye.

(Exploration des planètes, Larousse de Poche Couleur 1971)

---

1 Which is why the restrictive sense of our word "star", which excludes the planets, must not be applied to the Egyptian term *sb3*.

Venus Mecury		Mars Saturn Jupiter
INTERNAL PLANETS	EPAGOMENE DECANS	EXTERNAL PLANETS

Fig. 53 - The two groups of planets.

Nekhtnebef Sarcophagus (Berlin Museum, Neugebauer & Parker)

| Venus | Mercury | Mars | Saturn | Jupiter |

Fig. 54 - The planets at Dendera

(Budge & Brugsch)[2]

---

[2] E.A.W. Budge, *Gods of the Egyptians*, Vol 2, p. 303; H. Brugsch,
Thesaurus, p. 68.

2. Names and representations of the planets

1 - Mercury.

Mercury, the planet closest to the sun, is only visible from the Earth when the two move away from each other: it can then be seen for a few days only, in the evening, and again two months later, for a few days in the morning. Its name is 𓊃𓃀𓎼𓇼, *sbg*. The phases of matinal visibility of this planet, to which Seth is sometimes associated, could perhaps account for its qualification as "he who is in front of the boat of Rah".

2 - Venus.

The second inner planet is very brilliant and revolves at a greater distance from the sun than Mercury. Venus is visible during $9^{1}/4$ months in the morning, then $9^{1}/4$ months in the evening, with a total synodic period of 584 days[3].

On astronomical representations, Venus is placed farthest in the East, in the form of a bird *bnw*, or *b3ḥ*[4]. The planet bears several names[5]: 𓇼𓏏𓊖 or else, 𓇼 "morning divinity" as a morning star, and 𓇼𓏏𓊖 "unique star" as an evening star; due to its great brilliance, it is the first star to become visible after sundown and appears to be the only one while the sky is not yet completely dark.

3 - Jupiter.

Bright, but less brilliant than Venus, it moves slowly in the sky. Called 𓇼 "Southern Star", it also bears the name of 𓇼 . It appears as if it oscillates around a general position which is gliding slowly from West to East (an eastward movement of some 30° in a year and a month).

4 - Saturn.

Saturn, or 𓇼 "the Western Star which crosses the sky" is also called 𓇼 "Horus Bull of the Sky". This is the slowest of the planets, its synodic orbital cycle being 29 years and 167 days, and its movement (eastward by some 13° per annum) can hardly be perceived from one year to the next.

5 - Mars.

Its characteristic orange colour explains the name of Red Horus 𓇼 in graeco-romain times. It is also called 𓇼 "star of the Eastern sky", *Hr 3ḥty*, 𓇼 or 𓇼 "who navigates backwards", this latter name bearing witness to what is called the retrograde movement, observed approximately every 2 years in the case of Mars.

3. Course and retrograde movement of the planets

The planets are observed on planes neighbouring the ecliptic. Their direct movement is anti-clockwise, like that of the Earth. Due to the difference in their time of orbit, i.e. their speed[6], however, the normal direction of movement, if observed from the Earth, may appear to turn contrary (somewhat like a car appearing to move backwards when overtaken, see Fig. 55). Between these changes of direction, a planet may appear seemingly stationary at certain moments. In a general way, the planets appear to follow trajectories resembling a saw blade, occasionally even describing loops.

---

[3] Ptolemy (*Almagest*, book 10, chapter 4) points out that 5 Venus periods correspond to 8 Egyptian years: 584 days x 5 = 2920 days and 365 days x 8 = 2920 days. Van Oosterhout, *DE* 27, pp. 83-96, presents a treatise concerning the Venus cycle in which he recalls studies concerning the coincidence of the reappearance of Venus as the morning star with the heliacal rise of Sirius (every 243 years). He calculates that this incidence came to pass in A.D. 143, and believes that it is this event which was commemorated on the Aïon coin of Emperor Antoninus Pius. Sethe, *ZÄS* 66, p. 3, believes that that commemoration relates to the tetraery of the beginning of the sothic period.

[4] The bird *b3ḥ* which evokes the flooding, which could well be an argument in favour of Van Oosterhout's version.

[5] For the different variations of the planets' names see H. Brugsch, *Thesaurus*, pp. 65-68 and O. Neugebauer & R.A. Parker, *EAT* III, pp.175-182.

[6] The closer a planet is to the sun, the faster it moves, the shorter its orbit.

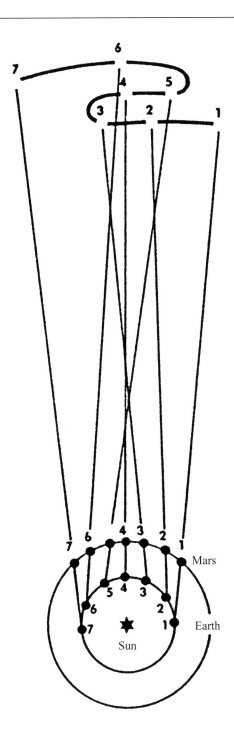

4. Planets and dating

The exact positioning of the planets certainly permits a precise dating, because their exact same position relative to one another only recurs after very long lapses of time. At Dendera, the zodiac has been studied for this purpose[7].

This is a most promising avenue of research[8], which could shed light on a number of questions concerning astronomy, the calendar, and even mythology. An example is the work of Krauss[9], who demonstrates that according to the dates of the Cairo Calendar[10], the period of Seth's activity must be linked to the periods of Mercury[11] and his phases, as a planet of both evening and morning. The eye of Horus is also set parallel to Venus, a point which puts a new light on certain passages in the texts of the Pyramids and those of the Coffins.

---

[7] E. Aubourg, *BIFAO* 95, pp. 1-10.

[8] The names of Southern Star for Jupiter, Eastern Star for Mars and Western Star for Saturn have no astronomical explanation, but could, however, relate to their position at some definite time which may be of interest.

[9] R. Krauss, *BSEG* 14, pp. 49-56.

[10] A.M. Bakir, *Cairo Calendar*.

[11] For Mercury's identification with Seth, see *EAT* III, p. 181.

Fig. 55 - The retrograde movement of the planets: example of Mars. (Exploration des planètes: Larousse de Poche Couleur 1971).

IV. The moon

1. Representations

On the astronomical tables, anything to do with the moon only appears on the second or lower register[1]. On the ceiling of Senmut's tomb (Fig. 56), the lunar deities, consigned to the extreme North, are totally separated from the great picture showing Sirius, the decans and the planets. Moreover, twelve big circles representing the twelve months of the year, arranged in three groups of four months for each season, are inserted between the upper, stellar register and the lower, lunar one. Each month is identified by its eponymic feast[2].

One is immediately struck in all calendary images by the difference in orientation between the figures of the upper, sothic register and the lower, lunar one. In the upper part, all figures move without exception from East to West, whilst the lunar divinities in the lower part are split into two groups either side of the centre, and move towards it (Fig. 57).

---

[1] This does not argue in favour of a calendar which was originally or essentially lunar; see also A. Spalinger, *CdE* 70, p. 119.

[2] For names of months and their divinities, see H. Brugsch, *Thesaurus*, pp. 472-473; L. Depuydt, *Civil Calendar and Lunar Calendar*, p. 116; A. Spalinger, *CdE* 70, p. 118. For the problems related to these months, and especially the 12th month, see Gardiner, *ZÄS* 43, pp. 136-144 and *RdE* 10, pp. 9-31; R.A. Parker, *Calendars*, p. 31 and *RdE* 11, pp. 85-107; R. Krauss, *Sothis und Monddaten*, p. 105 ff; L. Depuydt, *Civil Calendar and Lunar Calendar*, pp. 216-248; J. von Beckerath, *ZÄS* 120, pp. 17-22.

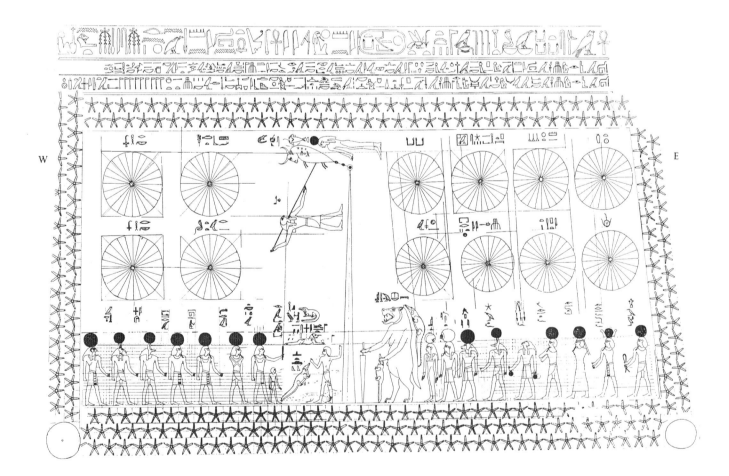

Fig. 56 - Months and lunar divinities on the Senmut ceiling.

This disposition could follow two aspects of the moon's course: first, the monthly cycle[3] - the new moon appearing in the West, the crescent and full moon, then the waning moon disappearing in the East; but secondly also the annual lunar cycle where each new moon seems to follow the sun in its movement[4]. In the representations, the lunar deities are clearly shown in relation to the constellations in the Northern sky.

[3] The moon takes a month to run approximately through the same movement as the sun in a year, but with a complex trajectory covering a vast part of the sky. This course across the stellar constellations seems to explain why the Egyptians, acording to Eudoxus cited by Proclus, had given the name "year" to a month.

[4] The point of the sun's rise, which runs through all the zodiacal constellations in one year, is situated North of the exact point East for 6 months, and then South of it for the following six months.

Fig. 57 - The two converging groups of lunar deities, Tomb of Seti I. (Photo Lehnert & Landrock, succ. Lambelet)

2. The monthly lunar cycle

The lunar or synodic month is the lapse of time separating two identical views of the moon (e.g. two new or full moons). Its duration is 29½ days[5].

The phases of the moon represent its various positions in relation to the sun and the Earth during its course around the latter (Fig. 58).

The figure above indicates only the Egyptian names of the four main phases, each being the occasion of a special feast. The cycle begins at the

[5] Precisely 29 days, 12 hours, 44 minutes, 2.9 seconds.

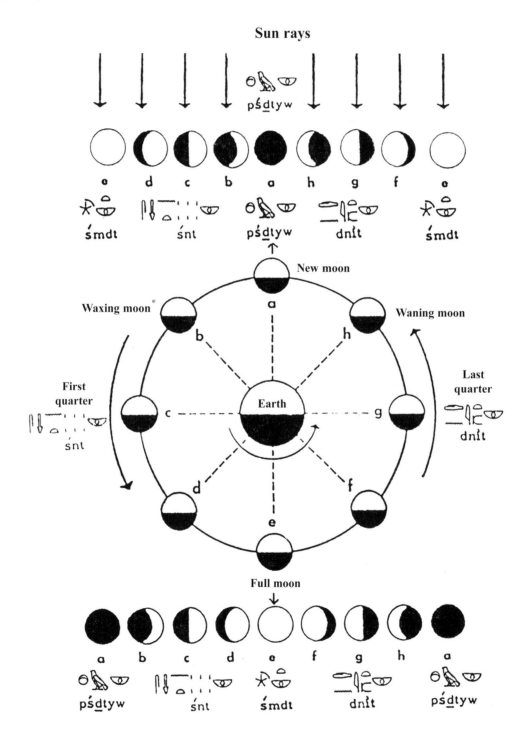

Fig. 58 - The phases of the lunar cycle
(a to h: aspects of the moon as seen from the Earth during one cycle).
(Exploration des planètes, Larousse de Poche Couleur 1971)

time of invisibility: the black moon, *Psdntyw*, the New Moon. The first quarter is the Feast of the 6th Day, *Snt*. The full moon is called *Smdt* or Feast of The 15th Day. The last quarter is named *dnit*. Each of the 30 lunar days has its name[6], and the lunar cycle has an eminent position in a cultual and mythological context.

The ascendant phase of the moon is sometimes represented by stairs of 14 steps[7], on which the gods of the Great Ennead of Karnak are standing. Each step represents one day of the ascendant phase of the moon: the gods of the Great Ennead penetrate one after another, one each day,

into the eye[8] to increase it. The Healthy Eye, presented on a *w3d* 𓊽 – which means "healthy", "flourishing" – is the full moon, i.e. the eye healed and recreated by Thoth[9] (Fig. 59).

---

[8] See P. Derchain, *RdE* 15, p. 23, fig. 5; P. Barguet, *RdE* 29, p. 15, text and Note 20; F.R. Herbin, *BIFAO* 82, pp. 240-246; F. Labrique, *BSFE* 140, p. 14 and *RdE* 49, p. 108 and Plate XXI.

[9] Thôt appears as a lunar symbol because he personifies everything right, exact and complete. We note that he is also the divinity of the 6th hour of the day (noon), the hour when the sun is precisely in the meridien.

---

[6] R.A. Parker (*Calendars*, pp. 9-23) has demonstrated that the month began with the invisibility. For the names of the lunar days see H. Brugsch, *Thesaurus*, pp. 46-48 and Parker, *Calendars*, pp. 11-12. For the lunar feasts see A. Spalinger, *BSEG* 19, pp. 25-40.

[7] According to Plutarch, the 14-16 days required to reconstitute the disk of the moon is related to the number of dispersed parts of Osiris' body: see P. Derchain, *La lune, mythes et rites*, p. 45.

Fig. 59 - The ascendant phase of the moon at Dendera (Budge)[10].

---

[10] E.A.W. Budge, Gods of the Egyptians, Vol. II, 1969, p. 321.

One scene in the Sokaris chapel at Dendera shows the full moon at the moment of its rise. The full moon does indeed rise in the East, just as the sun settles in the West. "*Khonsou-Ioh, light of the night, image of the left eye of Amon, rising at Bakht (i.e. the Orient) while Aton (the sun) is in Ankhtet (the Occident). Theben is flooded in their splendour, for the left eye receives its light from the right one as they reunite on the day of the two bulls*"[11]. The complete eye is shown in a net held by Thoth and Shu[12] (Fig. 60).

As regards the waning moon, assimilated to the decline of Osiris[13], it is evoked much more rarely.

3. The lunar year

The lunar year is composed of 354 days[14], 11 days less than the mobile year. This provokes a discrepancy in months on the one hand, with some months positioned astride two consecutive years[15], and on the other hand it creates a gap of lunar phases in relation to the 365 days of the mobile year.

R.A. Parker[16] states that only the intercalary months take the name of *Dhwty*. R. Krauss[17], however, contests this affirmation, and it would indeed seem more likely that *Dhwty*, together with

Tḥ were variations of the name of the first month.

As the rise of Sirius inaugurates the year, most authors agree that the beginning of the "lunar year" could only be defined in accordance with that rise[18]. As Spalinger[19] very justly points out, however, it is more than probable that the lunar feasts were celebrated **according to the real aspect of the moon** and not according to complicated calculations predetermined by the calendar.

Like the rise of Sothis, the lunar cycle, too, is related to the mobile year, which allows definition of the phases and recognises the phenomena which arrive when counting in entire days. In some texts, mention of a day in the civil year with the precise aspect of the moon can be found. This means that mobile and lunar dates are available; these are of great interest for the purpose of chronological cross-checking[20].

---

[18] R.A. Parker, *Calendars*, p. 31 ff.; R. Krauss, *Sothis und Monddaten*, p. 15 ff.; L. Depuydt, *Civil Calendar and Lunar Calendar*, p. 137 ff.

[19] A. Spalinger, *BSEG* 19, p. 40.

[20] For these double dates, see for example L. Depuydt, *Civil Calendar and Lunar Calendar*, pp. 140, 155, 163, 171-175.

---

[11] P. Derchain, *La Lune, mythes et rites*, p. 28 (URK VIII, 49 (61 b), Edfou 3, 208).

[12] P. Derchain, *RdE* 15, p. 16.

[13] E. Chassinat, *Le mystère d'Osiris au mois de Khoiak*, p. 281, Note 2. Concerning Khonsou Moon, it is said: "when he becomes a child again, he is an ardent bull, in his age, he is a castrated bull creating obscurity". For the association Osiris-Moon, see also P. Derchain, *La lune*, pp. 44-46 and G. Griffiths, *JEA* 62, 1976, pp. 153-159.

[14] 12 months of 29.5 days add up to 354 days.

[15] If the 1st lunar month begins after the 11th day of the year (about 2 times out of 3), the 12th lunar month will spill over into the following year. If it begins during the first 10 days, the first month of the following lunar year is astride the 2 years: see R.A. Parker, *Calendars*, p. 31; A. Spalinger, *SAK* 20, pp. 302-303 and *BSEG* 19, pp. 25-40; L. Depuydt, *Civil Calendar and Lunar Calendar*, pp. 41-45.

[16] R.A. Parker, *Calendars*, p. 31.

[17] R. Krauss, *Sothis und Monddaten*, p. 204.

Fig. 60 - Rise of the full moon. Denderah, Sokaris chapel, western wall. (from Dendera 2, plate 127 and Derchain)

Conclusion

Fig 61 - Akhenaton and Nofretete under the radiant sun, 18th dynasty, Egypt. Museum Cairo.

1. The principle of the gliding calendar

The Egyptian calendar, like our own, attributes 365¼ days to the year, which requires the count of an additional day every fourth year. The manner in which this additional day is treated characterises the great and essential difference between the Egyptian calendar and our own.

The Gregorian Calendar, which is our own, is a better, corrected version of the Julian calendar, but it is based on the same principle: the additional day is added as the 29th day of February of the bissextile or leap years.

The Egyptian Calendar takes account of the additional day, but without actually adding it. Instead, two calendars are made to glide one inside the other:

– **one, called fixed or sothic, of 365¼ days**,

permits the precise count of the years, whose beginning always coincides exactly with the heliacal rise of Sirius.

– **the other, called vague or mobile, has 365 days.**

These two years move in opposite directions (Fig.62) relative to each other, the discrepancy between them increasing by one day every four years. The full circle is completed in 1460 years, after which time the date of the rise of Sirius in the mobile year is once more the same as 1460 years before. This great sothic period of 1460 years, i.e. the time required for the date of the heliacal rise of Sirius to run through each day of the mobile year, is the direct manifest expression of the Gliding Calendar.

The drawback of this system is that the sothic-mobile couple imperatively needs to maintain the vague or mobile year, with the consequence of the unavoidable displacement of the seasons in that so-called mobile year, the gap reaching a maximum after 753 years. The great advantage of this calendar lies in the fact that all

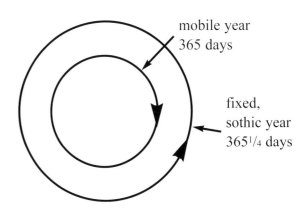

Fig. 62 - The system of the gliding calendar

necessary readjustments due to the intercalary days, i.e. the additions and modifications in our Gregorian Calendar, are needless: **the gliding system allows the periodical self-regulation of the astronomical cycles**, most notably the spontaneous return of equinoxes and solstices to their proper place, which renders it viable through uncounted millennia. **The entire structure rests on the choice of Sirius**, i.e. the only star which counts almost exactly 365¼ days between 2 heliacal rises. This avoids the fractions of days – the most difficult stumbling block for any calendaric construction – on the one hand, and it allows the concept of the two years – the fixed and the mobile – one inside the other.

The structure of this calendar is clearly based on the decans. It is organised around Sirius, the focal and dominant element of Egyptian astronomical representations, and rests on the civil or mobile year as the habitual one all through the history of the Egyptian civilisation.

2. Application to the Ramesseum

2. The axial disposition in the centre is the pivot around which the entire system is developed.

1. The horizontal disposition represents the different cycles, gliding one against the other and against the mobile year. The horizontal strips are, in fact, to be considered as circles[1], as on the Karnak clepsydra (Fig. 12).

---

[1] The notion of the cyclical calendar can also be found in F.R. Herbin, *Le Livre de Parcourir l'Eternité*, pp. 340-350 with a calendar-oriented table of feast days and comments pp. 351-364.

[2] There is not a single text which would enhance the suggestion that the months in the fixed year were numbered like those in the civil year. Some documents, among which the Papyrus Ebers, suggest, on the contrary, that they were designated by the name of the principal feast day.

1 - Ramesseum - horizontal disposition: the astronomical cycles

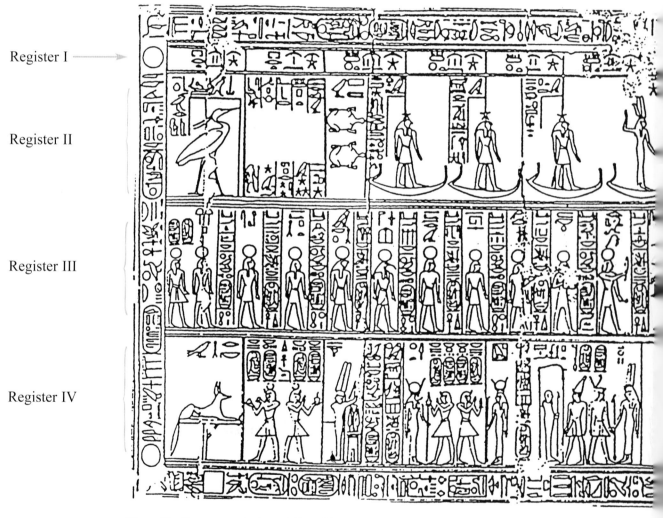

Register I

Register II

Register III

Register IV

Figure 63 - Ramesseum, horizontal disposition.

Register I   The mobile year, to which all cycles relate[2].

Register II   The sothic year, including the decanal cycle on the one hand, and the planets and the "decans" of the epagomenoi on the other.

Register III   The lunar year and monthly cycles.

Register IV   Pharaoh celebrating the divinities attached to the 12 feast days which divide the year into 12 months.

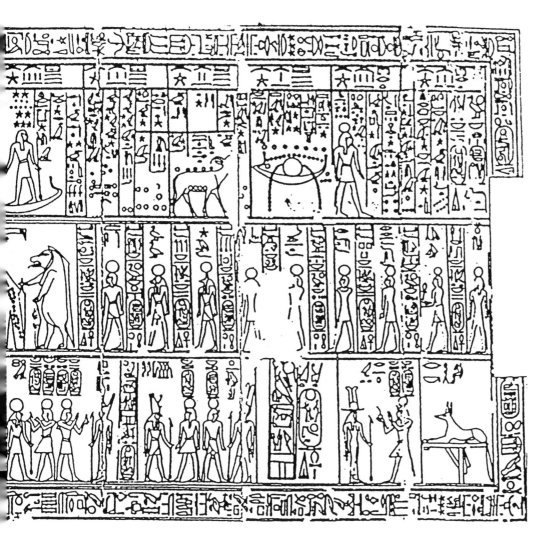

2 - Ramesseum – vertical axial disposition: Sirius, pivot of the system

Sirius inaugurating the sothic year and cycle, the decanal cycle, the lunar year

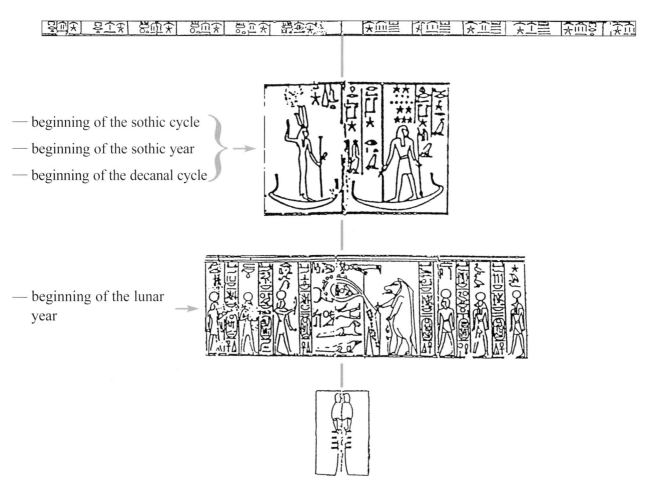

— beginning of the sothic cycle
— beginning of the sothic year
— beginning of the decanal cycle

— beginning of the lunar year

Fig. 64 - Ramesseum: central axial vertical disposition. Sirius at the origin of the astronomical cycles.

The precision, stability and perennity of the system are symbolised by Thoth, set up on the pillar *Dd* whose four levels could evoke the sothic four-year period (Fig. 65, 66).

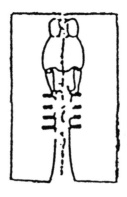

Fig. 65 - Thoth on the *Dd* pillar

The theory of the gliding calendar would explain that the mobile year was imperatively upheld, despite its inconveniences, over the entire period of Egyptian history, although the beginning of the year was clearly marked – as the texts indicate – by the heliacal rise of Sirius. It accounts for the displacement of dates and feast days between the fixed and the mobile year, and for the fact that the reappearance of Sirius takes place, according to the texts, either in the 5th epagomene (fixed year), or on the last day of *šmw* (mobile year).

And lastly and finally, this theory would explain the Egyptian calendar as a durable creation, a true work for eternity.

Fig. 66 - Seti I, guarantor of cosmic order, redressing the *Dd* pillar (Abydos)

Appendices

Appendix 1

Structure of the mobile year

The mobile year counts 365 days, separated into 3 seasons[1], each of 4 months (*3ḫt, prt, šmw*).

Each month is composed of 30 days. When dates are given, the months are designated by their seasons and the number 1 to 4 within them. In later times, they are designated by their eponymic feast.

To those 12 months of 30 days are added 5 epagomenoi or epagomene days, which are inserted between two successive years.

These 5 days are called "the five above the year". Although placed at the end of the year in the documents of the Middle and New Kingdoms, they were in the Old Kingdom[2] considered as preceding the year. But in any case they are "outside of the year" and the last day of the year is 30 Mesore, the 30th day of the 4th month of the 3rd season and not the 5th epagomene[3].

The names which are indicated here are those of the Greek and Coptic calendar[4]. The last month is designated in several documents, like the Ebers Papyrus, by 𝖄 , which means: New Year's Day, Beginning of the Year[5].

I	*3ḫt*		1st month	Thôth
			2nd "	Paophi
			3rd "	Athyr
			4th "	Choiak
II	*Prt*		1st month	Tybi
			2nd "	Mechir
			3rd "	Phamenoth
			4th "	Pharmouthi
III	*šmw*		1st month	Pachon
			2nd "	Payni
			3rd "	Epiphi
			4th "	Mesore

Fig. 67 - The mobile year.

---

[1] Contrary to our four seasons, separated by the 2 solstices and the 2 equinoxes, the 3 Egyptian seasons are not defined according to episodes of the annual solar cycle, but rather by the arrival of the flooding of the Nile.

[2] E. Meyer, *Chronologie égyptienne*, p. 8: see the inscription of Tehne of the Vth Dynasty (G. Frazer, Annales du Service des Antiquités III, p. 122; K. Sethe, Urkunden des Alten Reiches Nr 17); R.A. Parker, *Calendars*, p. 52.

[3] H. Brugsch, *Thesaurus*, p. 478.

[4] For the early names of months, see J. von Beckerath, *ZÄS* 120, pp. 17-22 and L. Depuydt, *Civil Calendar and Lunar Calendar*, plate p. 116.

[5] The term of *wp-rnpt* can apply to the mobile as well as to the sothic year, because it has more than one meaning: see A. Spalinger, *SAK* 17, pp. 289-294 and *Three studies*, pp. 45-49.

Appendix 2

The alexandrian year

The alexandrian calendar puts into effect the project envisaged by Ptolemy III in his Decree of Canopus, i.e. to fix the mobile year by the adjunction of a 6th epagomene every four years.

The chosen day of the year is not, however, the day of the heliacal rise of Sirius, as in the Decree of Canopus, but the 1st Thôt mobile, which at the time of the reform, fell 41 days after the rise of Sirius. The old mobile year is thus fixed by the insertion of an intercalary day, beginning on the 42nd day after the rise. In the year of the reform (25 B.C. = year 5 of Augustus), Sirius rose on the 25th day of the 3rd month of *šmw*.

From that year of 25 B.C. on, and in addition to the Julian Year, two fixed calendars co-existed, each of 365¼ days, and each with a 6th epagomene every 4 years:

- the sothic, inaugurated by the star's heliacal rise,
- the alexandrian, with the 1st Thôt falling 41 days after that rise.

Correspondence in the fixed years of 365¼ days				
Julian	**Sothic**		**Alexandrian**	
19 July	**1st day**	**1st Thôt (rise of Sothis)**	**325th day**	**25 Epiphi**
	42nd day	**12 Paophi**	**1st day**	**1st Thôt**

Fig. 68 - Corresponding dates between the 3 fixed years.

Abbreviations

BdE   Bibliothèque d'Etudes, Institut Français d'Archéologie Orientale, Cairo.

BES   Bulletin of the Egyptological Seminar, New York.

BIE   Bulletin de l'Institut d'Egypte, Cairo.

BIFAO   Bulletin de l'Institut Français d'Archéologie Orientale, Cairo.

BSEG   Bulletin de la Société d'Egyptologie de Genève, Geneva.

BSFE   Bulletin de la Société Française d'Egyptologie, Paris.

BSAC   Bulletin de la Société d'Archéologie Copte, Cairo.

CdE   Chronique d'Egypte, Bulletin périodique de la Fondation égyptologique Reine Elisabeth, Brussels.

DE   Discussions in Egyptology, Oxford.

EAT   Egyptian Astronomical Texts, O. Neugebauer and R.A. Parker, Providence and London, 1960-1969.

HPBM   Hieratic Papyri in the British Museum, London.

IFAO   Institut Français d'Archéologie Orientale, Cairo.

JARCE   Journal of the American Research Center in Egypt, New-York.

JEA   Journal of Egyptian Archaeology, London.

JHA   Journal for the History of Astronomy, Cambridge.

JNES   Journal of Near Eastern Studies, Chicago.

LÄ   Lexikon der Ägyptologie, Wiesbaden.

OLA   Orientalia lovaniensia analecta, Leeuwen.

OLZ   Orientalistische Literaturzeitung, Leipzig.

RdE   Revue d'Egyptologie, Paris.

SAK   Studien zur altägyptischen Kultur, Hamburg.

ZÄS   Zeitschrift für ägyptische Sprache und Altertumskunde, Leipzig-Berlin.

Bibliography

ALTENMÜLLER H., *Die Apotropaïa und die Götter Mittelägyptens*, Munich, 1965.

AUBOURG E., *La date de conception du zodiaque du temple d'Hathor à Denderah*, BIFAO 95, 1995, pp. 1-10.

BAKIR A.M., *The Cairo Calendar* n° 86637, Cairo, 1966.

BARGUET P., *Le rituel archaïque de fondation des temples de Médinet-Habou et de Louxor*, RdE 9, 1952, pp. 1-22.

BARGUET P., *Le cycle lunaire d'après deux textes d'Edfou*, RdE 29, 1977, pp. 14-20.

BARGUET P., *Remarques sur quelques scènes de la salle du sarcophage de Ramsès VI*, RdE 30, 1978, pp. 51-56.

BARTA W., *Die ägyptischen Monddaten und der 25-Jahr-Zyklus des Papyrus Carlsberg 9*, ZÄS 106, 1979, pp. 1-10.

von BECKERATH J., *Handbuch der ägyptischen Königsnamen*, Münchner Ägyptologische Studien 20, Munich/Berlin, 1984.

von BECKERATH J., *Bemerkungen zum ägyptischen Kalender*, I *Zur Entstehung des 365-tägigen Kalenders*, II *Zum Problem der Monatsnamen*, III *Zum Kalendarium des Papyrus Ebers*, ZÄS 120, 1993, pp. 7-22 and 131-136.

BEDIER S., *"Ein Stiftungsdekret Thutmosis' III aus Buto"*, in M. Minas et J. Seidler, Aspekte Spätägyptischer Kultur, Festschrift für Erich Winter zum 65, Geburtstag, Mayence, 1994, pp. 35-50.

BIOT J.B., *Traité élémentaire d'astronomie physique IV*, Paris, 1847.

BIOT J.B., *Recherches de quelques dates absolues qui peuvent se conclure des dates vagues*, Mémoires de l'Académie des Sciences, Paris, 1854.

BORCHARDT L., *Ein altägyptisches astronomisches Instrument*, ZÄS 37, 1899, pp. 10-17.

BORCHARDT L., *Der zweite Papyrusfund von Kahun und die zeitliche Festlegung des Mittleren Reiches der ägyptischen Geschichte*, ZÄS 37, 1899, pp. 89-103.

BORCHARDT L., *Die Altägyptische Zeitmessung*, Berlin, 1920.

BORCHARDT L., NEUGEBAUER O., *Beobachtung des Frühaufgangs des Sirius in Ägypten*, OLZ 29, 1926, col. 309-316, and OLZ 30, 1927, col. 441-448.

BOTHMER B., *Statuettes of w3ḏt as Ichneumon Coffins*, JNES 8, 1949, pp. 121-123.

BRUGSCH H., *Thesaurus Inscriptionum Aegyptiacarum: Altägyptische Inschriften*, Graz, 1968, first published Leipzig, 1883.

BRUNET DE PRESLE W., *Examen critique de la succession des dynasties égyptiennes*, Paris, 1850.

BUDGE E.A.W., *The Gods of the Egyptians*, New York, 1969, first published Chicago and London, 1904.

CAUVILLE S., *Dendera I*, OLA 81, Leeuwen, 1998.

CHABAS F., *Le Calendrier des jours fastes et néfastes de l'année égyptienne*, Paris, 1870.

CHASSINAT E., *Le Mystère d'Osiris au mois de Khoiak*, IFAO, Cairo, 1966, 1968.

CLAGETT M., *Ancient Egyptian Science* I, II, Philadelphia, 1992, 1995.

CLERE J.J., *Un texte astronomique de Tanis,* Kemi 10, 1949, pp. 3-27.

CLERE J.J., *Le système des décades du calendrier du Louvre (Louvre D 37)*, JNES 9, 1950, pp. 143-152.

COCHE C., *Une nouvelle statue de la déesse léontocéphale Ouadjet wp-t3wy*, RdE 22, 1970, pp. 51-62.

DEPUYDT L., *The function of the Ebers Calendar Concordance*, Orientalia 65, 1996, pp. 61-88.

DEPUYDT L., *Civil Calendar and Lunar Calendar in Ancient Egypt*, OLA 77, Leeuwen, 1997.

DERCHAIN P., *La Lune, mythes et rites*, Sources orientales 6, Paris, 1962, pp. 19-68.

DERCHAIN P., *La pêche de l'œil et les mystères d'Osiris à Dendara*, RdE 15, 1963, pp. 11-25.

DESROCHES-NOBLECOURT Ch., *Le petit temple d'Abou Simbel*, Cairo, 1968.

DESROCHES-NOBLECOURT Ch., *Le zodiaque de Pharaon*, Archéologia 292, 1993, pp. 21-45.

EBERS G., *Papyros Ebers*, Leipzig, 1875.

EISENLOHR A., *Der doppelte Kalender des Herrn Smith*, ZÄS 8, 1870, pp. 165-166.

GARDINER Sir A., *Mesore as First Month of The Egyptian Year*, ZÄS 43, 1906, pp. 136-144.

GARDINER Sir A., *The Problem of The Month Names*, RdE 10, 1955, pp.9-31.

GERMOND, P., *Les invocations à la bonne année au temple d'Edfou*, Aegyptiaca Helvetica 11, Geneva, 1986.

GODRON G., *Etudes sur l'époque archaïque*, BIFAO 57, 1958, pp. 143-155.

GOYON J.C., *Confirmation du pouvoir royal*, IFAO, Cairo & Brooklyn Museum, 1972.

GOYON G., *Le secret des bâtisseurs des grandes pyramides*, Paris, 1977.

GRIFFITHS G., *Osiris and The Moon in Iconography*, JEA 62, 1976, pp. 153-159.

GUTGUB A., *Remarques sur les dieux du nome tanitique à la Basse Epoque*, Kemi 16, 1962, pp. 42-75 and Kemi 17, 1964, pp. 35-60.

HABACHI L., HABACHI B., *The naos with the decades (Louvre D37) and the discovery of another fragment*, JNES 11, 1952, pp. 251-263.

HERBIN F.R., *Un hymne à la Lune croissante*, BIFAO 82, 1982, pp. 237-283.

HERBIN F.R., *Le livre de parcourir l'éternité*, OLA 58, Leeuwen, 1994.

HORNUNG E., *Untersuchungen zur Chronologie und Geschichte des Neuen Reiches*, Ägyptologische Abhandlungen 11, Wiesbaden, 1964.

HORNUNG E., *L'esprit du temps des Pharaons*, Zurich/Munich, 1989, French trsl. Paris, 1996.

HORNUNG E., *The Tomb of Pharaoh Seti* I, Zurich and Munich, 1991.

INGHAM M.F., *The length of the Sothic Cycle*, JEA 55, 1969, pp. 36-40.

ISLER M., *The Gnomon in Egyptian Antiquity*, JARCE 28, 1991, pp. 155-185.

KRAUSS R., *Sothis und Monddaten: Studien zur astronomischen und technischen Chronologie Altägyptens*, Hildesheimer Ägyptologische Beiträge 20, Hildesheim, 1985.

KRAUSS R., *Vorläufige Bemerkungen zu Seth und Horus/Horusauge im Kairener Tagewählkalender nebst Notizen zum Anfang des Kalendertages*, BSEG 14, 1990, pp. 49-56.

KRAUSS R., *Astronomische Konzepte und Jeinseitsvorstellungen in den Pyramidentexten*, Ägyptologische Abhandlungen 59, Wiesbaden, 1997.

LABRIQUE F., *Les escortes de la Lune dans le complexe lunaire de Khonsou à Karnak*, BSFE 140, 1997, pp. 13-26.

LABRIQUE F., *L'escorte de la Lune sur la porte d'Evergète à Karnak*, RdE 49, 1998, pp. 107-142.

LEITZ Ch., *Studien zur ägyptischen Astronomie*, Ägyptologische Abhandlungen 49, Wiesbaden, 1989/91.

LEITZ Ch., *Die Nacht des Kindes in seinem Nest in Dendara*, ZÄS 120, 1993, pp. 136-165.

LEITZ Ch., *Tagewählerei: Das Buch ḥȝt-nḥḥ-pḥ.wy-ḏt und verwandte Texte*, Ägyptologische Abhandlungen 55, Wiesbaden, 1994.

LEITZ Ch., *Altägyptische Sternuhren*, OLA 62, Leeuwen 1995.

LEPSIUS R., *Introduction à la chronologie des Egyptiens*, Revue Archéologique 6, 1849, pp. 525-539, 660-668.

LEPSIUS R., *Das bilingue Dekret von Canopus*, Berlin, 1866.

LETRONNE J.A., *Nouvelles recherches sur le calendrier des Anciens Egyptiens, sa nature, son histoire et son origine,* Mémoires de l'Académie des Inscriptions et Belles Lettres, T. 24, 1864.

LOCHER K., *Two Further Coffin Lids with Diagonal Star Clocks*, JHA 23, 1992, pp. 201-207.

LOCHER K., *New arguments for the celestial location of the decanal belt and for the origin of the S3ḥ-hieroglyph*, VI Congresso internazionale di Egittologia, Atti II, Turin, 1993, pp. 279-284.

LOCHER K., *Middle Kingdom Astronomical Coffin Lids, Extension of the Corpus from 12 to 17 Specimens Since Neugebauer & Parker*, Transactions of the 7th International Congress of Egyptologists, in C. EYRE, OLA, Leeuwen 1998, pp. 697-702.

LUFT U., *Die chronologische Fixierung des ägyptischen Mittleren Reiches nach dem Tempelarchiv von Illahun.* Österreichische Akademie der Wissenschaften, Vienna, 1992.

MEYER E., *Ägyptische Chronologie*, Abhandlungen der Königlich Preußischen Akademie der Wissenschaften, 1904, transl. A. Moret, Annales du Musée Guimet, Bibliothèque d'Etudes, Vol. 24, Paris, 1912.

MONTET P., *Le rituel de fondation des temples égyptiens*, Kemi 17, 1964, pp. 74-100.

NEUGEBAUER O., & VOLTEN A., *Untersuchungen zur antiken Astronomie IV. Ein demotischer astronomischer Papyrus (Pap. Carlsberg 9)*, Quellen und Studien zur Geschichte der Mathematik, Abt. B, Band 4, Berlin, 1938, pp. 383-406.

NEUGEBAUER O., & PARKER R.A., *Egyptian Astronomical Texts*, Providence & London, 1960/69.

van OOSTERHOUT, G.W., *Sirius, Venus and the Egyptian Calendar*, D.E. 27, 1993, pp. 83-96.

PARKER R.A., *The Calendars of Ancient Egypt.* Studies in Ancient Oriental Civilization 26, Chicago, 1950.

PARKER R.A., *The Problem of the Month-Names: A Reply*, RdE 11, 1957, pp. 85-107.

PEET E., *The Rhind Mathematical Papyrus*, London, 1923.

PETRIE Sir W., *Royal Tombs I & II*, London, 1900 and 1901.

PIERRET P., *Recueil d'inscriptions inédites du Musée du Louvre* II, Paris, 1878, p.73.

POSENER-KRIEGER P., *Les Archives du temple funéraire de Néferirkarë-Kakaï (Les Papyrus d'Abousir)*, HPBM V, London, 1968 and BdE 65, IFAO, Cairo, 1976.

de ROUGE E., *Mémoires sur quelques phénomènes célestes*, Revue d'Archéologie, Vol. 9, 1852, pp. 653-691.

SAUNERON S., *Les fêtes religieuses d'Esna aux derniers siècles du paganisme*, Esna V, IFAO, Cairo, 1962.

SCHLOTT A., *Die Ausmaße Ägyptens nach altägyptischen Texten*, Darmstadt, 1969.

SCHOTT S., *Altägyptische Festdaten*, Akademie der Wissenschaften und der Literatur in Mainz, Wiesbaden, 1950.

SETHE K., *Sethi I und die Erneuerung der Hundssternperiode*, ZÄS 66, 1930, pp. 1-7.

SLOLEY R.W., *Primitive Methods of Measuring Time*, JEA 17, 1931, pp. 166-178.

SPALINGER A., *A Return to Papyrus Ebers*, BES 10, 1989-1990, pp. 137-144.

SPALINGER A., *A Remark on Renewal*, SAK 17, 1990, pp. 289-294.

SPALINGER A., *Night into Day*, ZÄS 119/2, 1992, pp. 144-156.

SPALINGER A., *Three Studies on Egyptian Feasts and their Chronological Implications*, Baltimore, 1992.

SPALINGER A., *A Chronological Analysis of the Feast of Tḥy*, SAK 20, 1993, pp. 289-303.

SPALINGER A. (editor), *Revolutions in Time: Studies in Ancient Egyptian Calendrics*, Varia Aegyptiaca I, supplément 6, San Antonio, Texas, 1, 1994.

SPALINGER A., *Some Remarks on the Epagomenal Days in Ancient Egypt*, JNES 54, 1995, pp. 33-47.

SPALINGER A., *Sothis and Official Calendar Texts*, Varia Aegyptiaca 10, 2/3, 1995, pp. 175-183.

SPALINGER A., *Month Representations*, CdE 70, 1995, pp. 110-22.

SPALINGER A., *The Lunar System in Festival Calendars: From the New Kingdom Onwards*, BSEG 19, 1995, pp. 25-40.

SPALINGER A., *The Private Feast Lists of Ancient Egypt*, Ägyptologische Abhandlungen 57, Wiesbaden, 1996.

SPALINGER A., *The Festival Structure of Thutmose III's Buto Stele*, JARCE 33, 1996, pp. 69-76.

SYMONS A., *Shadow Clocks and Sloping Sundials of the Egyptian New Kingdom and Late Period: Usage, Development and Structure*, BSS 98, 3, 1998, pp. 30-36.

THOMAS E., *Solar barks Prow to Prow*, JEA 42, 1956, pp. 65-79.

VANDIER J., *Ouadjet et l'Horus léontocéphale de Bouto*, Extrait des monuments et mémoires de l'Académie des Inscriptions et Belles Lettres, Vol. 55, Paris, 1967, pp. 7-75.

WEILL R., *Bases, méthodes et résultats de la chronologie égyptienne*, Paris, 1926 and *Compléments*, Paris, 1928.

WELLS R.A., *Sothis and the Satet Temple at Elephantine*, SAK 12, 1985, pp. 255-302

WELLS R.A., *The 5th Dynasty Sun Temples at Abu Ghurab as Old Kingdom Star Clocks: Examples of Applied Ancient Egyptian Astronomy*, BSAK 4, 1990, pp. 95-104.

WELLS R.A., *The Mythology of Nut and the Birth of Ra*, SAK 19, 1992, pp. 305-321.

WELLS R.A., *Origin of the Hour and the Gates of the Douat*, SAK 20, 1993, pp. 305-326.

YOYOTTE J., *A propos du Naos des décades*, JNES 13, 1954, pp. 79-82.

YOYOTTE J., *Une monumentale litanie de granit*, BSFE 87-88, 1980, pp. 47-75.

YOYOTTE J., CHARVET P., GOMPERTZ S., *Strabon, Le Voyage en Egypte*, Paris 1997.

List and references of figures and photographs

Front cover: Thôt, God of Science, Master of Time, Luxor, 19th dynasty,
        (Photo by the author).
Rear cover: Sechat, Mistress of Writing and Archives, Luxor, 19th dynasty,
        (Photo by the author).

Photos and figures